'Did you think I'd find your charms so irresistible that I'd install you in my house, not as a housekeeper, but as my lover?' questioned Saul.

'How dare you!' Penny was on her feet, eyes flashing sapphire fury. 'How dare you think for one moment that I'd come to you with such an outrageous suggestion!'

Just because her twin sister had once lost her heart to him, he had no grounds for believing she would react in the same way. But he was right about one thing. She hadn't come just to get a job as housekeeper. It wouldn't be enough to convince a court of her total suitability to accept full responsibility for Lucy. She wanted more, much more. And now was the time to admit it.

'What I want,' she said clearly, holding her head high, meeting his challenging stare with the steady blaze of blue eyes, 'what I want from you, Mr van Diemen, is marriage. I want to become your wife.'

DESPERATE REMEDY

BY
ANGELA WELLS

MILLS & BOON LIMITED
ETON HOUSE   18–24 PARADISE ROAD
RICHMOND   SURREY   TW9 1SR

*First published in Great Britain 1987
by Mills & Boon Limited*

© Angela Wells 1987

*Australian copyright 1987
Philippine copyright 1987
This edition 1987*

ISBN 0 263 75820 6

*Set in Times 10 on 11½ pt.
01-1187-50705*

*Computer typeset by SB Datagraphics,
Colchester, Essex*

*Printed and bound in Great Britain by
Collins, Glasgow*

CHAPTER ONE

PENNY stared blankly out of the window as the taxi driver weaved and sliced through the traffic behind the main thoroughfares of London's West End where the offices of the van Diemen Consultancy were located.

Outside the steady November drizzle coated the thronged pavements with a patina of mud. The inclement weather justified the extravagance of a cab, she consoled herself, for apart from being uncertain how to reach her destination on foot, the last thing she wanted was to arrive with splodges of mud all over her nylons. She needed every grain of confidence she still possessed—and after the hours of tossing and turning she'd spent in bed the previous night, that was precious little!

She heaved a deep sigh, clasping her slender hands together in a vain attempt to still their trembling. She certainly wasn't looking forward to what she had to do. If Saul van Diemen had been unavailable when she'd phoned earlier that morning, the odds were she would have abandoned her enterprise entirely, she admitted to herself. The fact of his being there and free to see her had solidified her resolve.

Wasn't there a saying that desperate ills required a desperate remedy? And wasn't she facing the most desperate ill of her life at that moment?

She flicked a speck of dust from the skirt of her black woollen dress. Six weeks after the horrific disaster of the Mexican earthquake that had robbed her of a dearly loved twin sister and a respected and admired brother-in-law it still seemed natural to display externally in her dress the dark emptiness of grief that continued to erode her internally.

If only Michael hadn't been sent to Mexico on business by Saul van Diemen . . . if only Tuppy hadn't been invited by their Mexican hosts to accompany him . . . if only she, Penny, hadn't already shown her capabilities of looking after their baby daughter for the three days her sister had had to go back into hospital for a minor 'gynae' repair when Lucy had been four months old . . . if only she hadn't argued so eagerly when Tuppy had expressed doubts about exposing her baby daughter to the unknown germs of Mexico that she, Penny, would love to move into their flat and look after the child for them while they enjoyed the honeymoon they had never had . . . if only they hadn't loved and trusted her so much and Tuppy had let Michael go alone . . . But no—that would be wishing widowhood on her sister . . .

Desperately Penny forced her mind away from useless conjectures. She had to face the facts and act accordingly. She sat a little straighter on the edge of the seat as resolve tensed her spine. She'd never let her twin down when she'd needed her . . . and she wasn't starting now—whatever the price to her pride!

Damn it, she wouldn't cry! She had wept long and hard enough over the past few weeks to know what a useless process it was. It inflamed her nose, made her eyes swell, turned her creamy skin blotchy and gave her an appalling headache!

Her long slender fingers with their oval unpainted nails touched the cuff of her dress. It was an ideal garment for the ordeal ahead, clothing her discreetly from neck to knee, from shoulder to wrist.

A warm wave of colour invaded her pale cheeks. Only six weeks ago Saul's impertinent eyes had travelled with a mocking perception over her half-naked body. The memory of his insolent gaze had haunted her shamefully, until tragedy had relegated the incident to insignificance. Now the shame she had felt returned with its former causticity. At least, she thought grimly, he would have no reason to smirk at her appearance today!

Black didn't flatter her; the colour made her skin look wan by comparison and did nothing to enhance the shining fall of her deep auburn hair. She'd thought twice about applying make-up, deciding finally for the sake of her own self-esteem to add a little colour to her lips and to attempt to cover up the dark circles beneath her eyes with a tinted make-up base. Even the string of pearls at her throat, a twenty-first birthday present from Tuppy last year, had been worn because they formed a tangible link with her dead sister, rather than as an aid to her vanity.

As the taxi drew into the kerb outside a converted basement house, its steps freshly whitened despite the rain, its black rails gleaming, Penny knew she had arrived, even before seeing the neat brass plate confirming that this smartly decorated and restored mansion housed the van Diemen empire.

'Ta, luv!' The cab driver sketched her a cheerful salute as he pocketed her fare and tip. 'Have a nice day!'

A smile lifted the corners of her pretty mouth. If he only knew the ordeal lying ahead of her, he would have realised just how much she appreciated his cheerful exhortation.

Well, it was no good standing here watching the taxi

move away. One deep breath, an adjustment of her short jacket and she was entering the building before her jangling nerves could override her determination.

'Miss Penelope Kingston?' An attractive blonde receptionist rose instantly to greet her with a politely enquiring smile, then as Penny nodded, 'Mr van Diemen is expecting you—just go straight in.' She indicated a nearby unmarked door.

So soon? Penny gulped. She'd been hoping to have a few moments to gather her thoughts, to rehearse mentally for the umpteenth time what she'd come to ask him. A quick glance at her watch confirmed that she was a few minutes later than the time he had suggested. She took another deep breath, praying it would calm the erratic beating of her heart. Saul van Diemen was her last chance. Her only chance: and she wished with all her heart it could have been anyone else but him! To be late would do her cause no good at all.

Her hand on his door, she counted up to three, raised her small, determined chin a little higher, muttered a brief silent prayer and went in.

'This is a pleasant surprise, Penny.' He was coming towards her across the large room, as tall and powerful as she remembered, dark-haired, grey-eyed, his positive masculine aura dominating his surroundings, a polite smile on his lips. 'Let me take your coat.' He continued speaking in his deep pleasant voice as she allowed him to lift the jacket from her rigidly held shoulders. 'If only I'd known earlier you were coming I'd have cancelled my lunch date.'

'My purpose in coming is business, not social,' she said stiffly, watching as he placed her jacket over the back of a chair, before obeying his unspoken invitation to seat herself on the cream leather chesterfield facing his imposing desk.

'The two aren't necessarily incompatible,' he returned with an easy hospitality, seating himself in the swivel chair behind the desk, pushing it back so he could stretch out his long legs in a relaxed attitude while he allowed his gaze to dwell on the strained lines of her pale face.

As if what he read there puzzled him, his eyes narrowed speculatively. 'Despite your decision not to deal with me personally in respect of Michael's affairs, as I told you at the time, the services of my experts are always freely available to you or your legal representative at any time. You only have to ask.'

'Yes.' Penny stared down at her hands tightly clasped in her lap, knowing she'd been extremely ungracious in her attitude towards the man who now regarded her with unfeigned interest. However much he had merited her rebuff, it could hardly have endeared her to him. 'Thank you.'

Aware that he was waiting for her to continue, one dark eyebrow raised in quizzical invitation, Penny cleared her throat hesitantly.

'There aren't any problems with the estate. Even though neither Tuppy nor Michael left a will, I've been granted letters of administration. There was no one else, you see . . .' Her voice tailed away. No one but ten-month-old Lucy. Quickly she fought back incipient tears. 'In the letter you wrote to me at the time you also offered me your personal help.' His blandly assessing regard silently encouraged her to ask the question he must have guessed hovered on her tongue. 'Is that offer still open?'

Saul smiled, and it transfigured his hard-boned face. The harsh almost careworn lines of cheek and jaw lifted, the sternness of the mouth relaxed, filling and curving as Penny glimpsed the gleaming whiteness of well-cared-for teeth. Oddly, rather than relaxing at his response, she felt the muscles of her diaphram tighten in instinctive alarm.

'It's certainly negotiable.' It was a cautious reply, but at least he was listening. 'What exactly do you have in mind—a job, a loan . . .?'

She knew she was breathing faster, was conscious of his glance lingering on the nervous rise and fall of her breasts beneath the dark wool covering.

'Not exactly—it was something Michael said at Lucy's christening. He said you were reluctantly putting your lovely house back on the market after Christmas because you couldn't get a suitable live-in housekeeper to look after it in the way it deserved and the way you wanted it to be.'

Her anxious eyes beseeched his agreement of her surmise, fruitlessly.

'And?'

There was nothing in the soft question to alarm her, yet Penny felt the hairs on the back of her neck rise.

'And—if the job is still available, I'd like to apply for it . . . and bring Lucy with me.'

She could feel the dampness of perspiration veiling her forehead, her upper lips, the soft cushioned under-surfaces of her breasts as her nerves betrayed her. And she still hadn't set more than a foot inside the minefield ahead of her!

Outside a car pulled up with the muted protest of tyres. Inside the room it was quiet; remarkably so.

'It's Lucy, you see . . .' The bleak intensity of Saul's grey-eyed stare drove her to further explanation. 'She's been put into voluntary care and I've got no legal rights to claim her.' Pain deepened the darkness of her pupils, made her throat ache with unbearable tension. 'The only thing I can do is ask the courts to appoint me as her guardian . . . persuade them that it will be the best thing to ensure her happiness.'

'And will it be, do you think?' Penny quailed at the deceptively gentle question as the stern-faced man opposite her surveyed her with no sign of sympathy. 'Why was she taken away from you in the first place?'

Blood flooded into her face. Was he suggesting she'd wilfully neglected her baby niece?

'I was ill,' she flared back at him, her voice snapping in anger. Because Michael's flat had been on a short-term lease she'd had to take Lucy back to her own small apartment. It had been a terrible struggle trying to fit the cot and all the baby paraphernalia into her own bedroom, but she'd managed it—and without help! At first when the shivering fits started she had dismissed them as being reaction to circumstances, but when they were followed by spells of burning fever she had recognised the truth.

'It was influenza—a particularly virulent strain—and it knocked me off my feet. Within the first few hours I knew I wouldn't be able to care for her and it would have been irresponsible, even criminal, to expose her to the infection.' A spark of hostility in her blue eyes dared Saul to belittle the severity of her illness or challenge her decision, but his brooding gaze merely encouraged her to continue. She did so, her voice husky with the memory of what had happened.

'I phoned the doctor and he came over immediately and arranged for Lucy to be put in voluntary care.' She paused, fighting back a surge of unwelcome emotion.

The one thing she didn't mean to have recourse to was tears! It was Saul's sense of honour she intended to appeal to, not his tender heart. As far as she'd been able to ascertain, the latter's existence was in some doubt anyway!

'It was three weeks before I could get about again. That's when I found out she wasn't going to be given back to me.'

'So you want to use my house as a base from which to carry out your negotiations. Is that it?' He gave her a level look.

'What I have in mind is a business proposition which would benefit all parties,' Penny responded eagerly, a bright spot of colour in each cheek.

'Go on,' drawled Saul encouragingly. 'You have my entire attention.'

For a moment she hesitated, wishing she could catch a glimmer of compassion on the enigmatic face of the man watching her with his steady gaze, but he was giving nothing away.

'Well, it's like this.' Her hands twisted nervously together. 'If I'm to persuade the authorities I can look after Lucy I need a larger place to live. Somewhere I can continue with my work at the same time as I'm caring for her. My own place is much too small and I can't afford anything larger yet, not until I've built up my business.'

There was no need to spell out the details. Saul already knew she earned her living by carrying out commissioned glass-engraving, supplying exquisite rose bowls and glasses among other things to celebrate special events and anniversaries. At the christening he had congratulated her on the quality of her work as evidenced on the crystal bowl she had designed for her godchild . . .

their godchild. That was what she had to remember. Saul might not be related to Lucy by blood, but by accepting the role of godfather he had committed himself to caring for Lucy's welfare!

'So I thought if I were to become your housekeeper you could provide me with the extra space I need, and in return I'd work under your supervision in the house— cook, clean . . . do everything you need to make it run smoothly, and it wouldn't cost you anything.'

'No?' He watched her, smiling. 'I doubt that very much . . . even if the payment was loss of tranquillity and peace of mind.'

Penny bit her lip, sensing his antagonism, but then she'd never expected it to be easy.

'Tell me, Penny—what makes you think being a housekeeper would make you sufficiently desirable in the eyes of the authorities to make you a surrogate mother, hmm?' He didn't wait for her answer. 'Housekeepers can be dismissed at a moment's notice if they're unsatisfactory.'

The faint twist of his mouth suggested that as far as she was concerned that could be a distinct possibility.

'Or were you expecting me to give you some degree of security by guaranteeing your position regardless?' Dark brows raised inviting her reply.

'Not exactly,' she wavered. Dear God, this was much harder than she'd imagined!

'Well, then,' he persisted, leaning across the desk, grey eyes glinting with malicious delight. 'Let's see if I can guess. You obviously know I have a healthy income and no permanent companion in my bed at nights. Could it be that you thought of guaranteeing your security by helping me spend the former and fill the latter? Did you think I'd find your charms so irresistible I'd install you in my house, not as a housekeeper, but as my lover?'

'How dare you!' Penny was on her feet, eyes flashing sapphire fury, scarlet wedges of anger emblazoned on her cheeks. 'How dare you think for one moment I'd come to you with such an outrageous suggestion!'

She was shaking as a mixture of anxiety and temper caused her heart to thunder beneath her slender ribcage. Just because her twin sister had once lost her heart to him, he had no grounds for believing she would react in the same way. But he was right about one thing. She hadn't come just to get a job as housekeeper.

It wouldn't be enough to convince a court of her total suitability to accept full responsibility for her darling Lucy. She'd wanted more, much more. And now was the time to admit it.

'What I want,' she said clearly and succinctly, holding her head high, meeting his challenging stare with the steady blaze of blue eyes, 'what I want from you, Mr van Diemen, is marriage. I want to become your wife.'

CHAPTER TWO

HER REWARD was the total look of blank astonishment that froze Saul's features, leaving him with an expression of disbelief as potent as if she'd just punched him in the solar plexus.

Her penalty was the sudden uncontrollable weakness in her legs that forced her to sit down again before she crumpled in an undignified heap at his feet.

It was his own fault, she told herself defiantly. She'd meant to approach her plan slowly and reasonably. It had been his unfair provocation that had forced her into this untimely declaration.

'Forgive me ... I obviously underestimated your ambition!' Saul had recovered his equilibrium first and was surveying her with a piercing attention. Almost as if behind that clear grey-eyed gaze he was mentally stripping her.

Beneath his intense cynosure Penny struggled to keep her dignity.

'Don't misunderstand me.' She tossed her auburn head with an unconscious gesture of arrogance. 'All I'm suggesting is a temporary arrangement of convenience to last until I've built up enough capital to get established in a large enough place of my own.' She lifted one shoulder negligently, trying to present a far more confident image than her erratic pulses portrayed. 'Say a year ... eighteen months at the most.'

'And then what?' Saul's grey eyes were implacable,

trapping her attention with their coldness.

Penny's chin lifted to meet the muted hostility of the question. 'A quiet annulment, after which Lucy and I would disappear completely from your life.'

'Leaving me without a housekeeper?'

Unsure whether it was a serious question or not, Penny didn't flounder. 'By that time I'd have the house running exactly as you wanted it. It would be part of our contract that before I left I'd find a successor for the job and school her into your habits and preferences so the changeover would be absolutely smooth.

'Oh, don't you see?' Her voice gained animation as she leaned forward slightly, wide blue eyes fastened on Saul's attentive face. 'I know it's an unorthodox idea, but it's the perfect solution for all of us! You'll get your house run just the way you want it without having to employ expensive domestic labour. And in return for the use of a couple of rooms I'll provide the full services of a housekeeper.'

Her face flushed with the excitement of explaining the carefully thought out plan, her eyes took on an added sparkle. 'You won't have to keep us, of course. I can support myself and Lucy will be provided for from Michael's insurances.' Another thought occurred to her. 'Actually, financially, you'd benefit, because while we were living with you, you could claim for both of us against your income tax!'

Ignoring the frown that had creased his brow at her last remark, Penny rushed on, determined to spell out all the advantages as she saw them while he was still listening to her. 'It's such a large house, I'd guarantee we wouldn't intrude on your privacy,' she assured him happily. 'It's just your pastoral patronage I need to

influence a court of law that I should have care of Lucy.'
She paused slightly to add emphasis to her next sentence.
'Naturally, since the marriage would only exist on paper,
you'd be totally free to lead your own personal life.'

Heaven forbid he might think she'd stop him
satisfying his male needs elsewhere—provided of course
that, for Lucy's sake, he did so discreetly.

Saul van Diemen was attractive in the way men of his
stature inevitably were. Jungle predators, tall, well-
formed, successful in everything they undertook, they
looked good, moved well, and lesser men stood aside to
let them pass. Lions like that would always have their
pride of females. It was important Saul should know she
was aware of his life-style and accepted that it would
continue if he saw the advantages of making her his
nominal wife.

'My own personal life?' Dark brows lifted as firm lips
mused on the phrase. 'By which I gather you mean I will
be allowed to enjoy other female companionship of an
intimate nature on a casual basis?'

Penny accorded him a swift smile of agreement. 'Ours
would only be a convenient arrangement—no ties, no
obligation on your side at all.'

'How very considerate of you!' His smile, she
recognised as her heart plummeted, was like the smile on
the face of the tiger . . . relentless and voracious. 'Did it
never occur to you that I might have imminent plans of
my own in that direction . . . for a permanent
relationship?'

'No, not really.' She hastened to justify her scheme.
'Michael told me that since your marriage broke up
several years ago you haven't been interested in serious
relationships. He said you were . . . were . . .' She faltered

at the ominous darkening of his expression.

'Embittered?' he queried sardonically. 'Is that the word you were looking for? Or "disenchanted"? Or did your brother-in-law suggest that the memory of a disastrous union when I was many years younger had lessened my appetite for enjoyment of the opposite sex?'

Quickly Penny flew to Michael's defence, annoyed with herself for referring to what had been said to her in confidence. 'Michael always spoke about you with the highest respect and admiration.' She gave a short laugh, remembering the younger man's awe. 'Anyone would have thought you were a composite of Isambard Kingdom Brunel and Leonardo da Vinci, the way he sang your praises! It was just that he considered himself your friend and wanted you to be happy.'

What Michael had in fact said was that his brilliant consultant engineer boss was rumoured as being unlikely ever to trust a woman again after the much publicised antics of his first wife! But she certainly wasn't going to repeat *that* remark. She'd been sufficiently indiscreet as it was, and Saul's scowl warned her that he'd heard enough.

'Michael *was* my friend.' She noticed the whitened knuckles of his clenched fist. 'So was your sister.' A latent anger dared her to question the assertion.

'Yes, I know.' Briefly Penny lowered her lashes, unwilling to dwell on the flash of pain she had seen traverse Saul's face.

'Do you?' The question was ringed with bitterness. 'I wonder just how much you do know.'

Penny sucked in her breath. It was only yesterday she had discovered the reference to Saul in Tuppy's diary. 'Met Saul van D,' Tuppy had written. 'Had dinner with

him—wow! Never guessed I'd end up in his bed!!!!'
Then later, much later, her sister had written, 'Saul came
to see me—begged me to reconsider marriage!'

Suppose she were to say to the harsh-faced man
glowering at her across the expensive stretch of executive
desk, 'I know you loved my sister and lost her to your best
friend. I know you continued to support and encourage
Michael in his career: that you agreed to be godfather to
his child—bought her an expensive christening gift—
lent your fabulous country house for a big celebration
party afterwards. And because I *do* know all these things
I'd *hoped* you'd see how impossible it is for Lucy to be put
into care when with your help I can claim her and make a
life for her and love her . . .'

Instead she said simply, 'Enough to ask you for your
support until I can get on my feet.'

Slowly Saul rose to his feet, moving forward until he
reached the edge of the desk nearest to her, where he
supported himself on one lean buttock, folding his arms
casually across his broad chest.

'And while you remain "off your feet", so to speak, I
shall be expected to turn a blind eye to the coming and
going of the men who put you in that position, is that it?'

For a moment Penny was stunned by the harsh
suggestiveness behind the question, before she rushed in
to defend herself, infuriated by his deliberately misusing
her colloquialism. 'Of course not! I've no personal life in
the sense you imply—and I want none. At the moment
the most important thing in my life is getting Lucy back!'

'And you chose me to be the instrument of your
persuasion . . . your deceit, hmm?'

Penny felt the rebuff in his voice, winced at its
hostility. But she mustn't allow herself to be cowed by the

simmering anger that had hardened Saul's jaw and turned his eyes into glacial chips.

'I thought it worth giving you the opportunity of helping me, yes! I believed you might be interested in Lucy's future!' Her eyes were stormy, her soft lips quivering with hurt and disappointment. 'After all, you did agree to be her godfather, didn't you? I thought you might feel you had a duty towards her. Or did you think the casual gift of a gold ingot discharged all your responsibilities?'

She stopped suddenly as her voice began to shake. The man was impossible to reason with!

'Is that all?' The narrowed eyes that met her own were unreadable, and suddenly Penny was filled with the need to hit back, to hurt him as much as his callous insinuations had wounded her.

'No, it's not,' she flung back at him. 'There was one more reason I came to you. I thought you might remember that if it hadn't been for your sending Michael to Mexico in the first place, Lucy wouldn't be an orphan now!'

As an indictment for murder it was neither fair not justified, but right at that moment Penny couldn't have cared less. Her face flushed with anger, she jumped to her feet, determined not to stay another moment.

'Sit down!'

Saul hadn't moved, but such was his authority that as their eyes locked in a silent duel Penny froze, petrified at the power of his barked command.

'I've nothing more to say.' Her throat was dry with nerves. Deliberately she disobeyed him, remaining rooted to the spot.

'But I have.' Saul's tone was scathing. 'I've let you have

your say, and now you're going to sit down and listen to me.'

For one moment she considered defying him, then she read the threat behind those cold grey eyes that if she refused to sit down voluntarily he would personally ensure she did. Reluctantly she chose the lesser evil, shrugging her shoulders and resuming her seat with an air of assumed indifference.

'Right!' Saul stood up, taking a few steps towards her. 'Now it's my turn.'

She didn't want to look at him, but the power of that icy glare was inescapable. Unwillingly Penny shivered, swallowing her dismay, as he allowed his gaze to pass over her in contemptuous dismissal.

'I am fully aware of my obligations towards my goddaughter and I have every intention of discharging them to the best of my ability.' He paused, drew in a deep breath. 'And that means I would prefer to see Lucy brought up in good foster-home rather than agree to your plan. I have no wish to see the child raised in the Bohemian way of life you so obviously enjoy because of your present whim to sample the vicarious joys of motherhood. In fact, my arrogant little godmother, I believe you're irresponsible and the last person I'd sponsor to be Lucy's guardian.'

'Oh!' She was on her feet, facing him, as his cruel words stabbed her like a dagger, the hot blood rising to her face. To turn down her plan was one thing. To justify his action on such specious grounds was something else! Bohemian indeed! Caught between laughter and tears at the injustice of his raw condemnation, she opened her mouth to refute it. Before she could utter one word in her own defence Saul had shortened the remaining distance between them, hard hands gripping her shoulders as he spoke with a quiet fury.

'Did you think my memory was so short I'd forget the first time we met?' He stared at the demure black dress. 'That little number you're wearing now may not be nearly so alluring as the outfit you wore to the christening, but it does nothing to blunt the recollections I have of what it conceals!'

An involuntary shiver ran up Penny's spine as she was forcibly reminded of the events she had striven so hard to block out of her mind.

Tuppy had surprised her on the morning of Lucy's christening with what she called the 'godmother's gift', a beautiful and expensive dress of dark blue crêpe with the loving exhortation that she should wear it to the ceremony. Low-cut and tightly fitted to the waist above a bias-cut skirt, it had been incredibly flattering to Penny's high rounded breasts and curving waist. It had also been the cause of the greatest humiliation of her life!

'The dress was a gift . . .' Her eyes met Saul's with a flash of indignation as she began the explanation his taunts demanded.

'And one which you couldn't wait to take off for the giver's pleasure, eh?'

'No!' The denial was an explosion of anger and resentment.

She *had* taken the dress off: but not for any man's gratification. Used to wearing loose casual clothes, she had soon found her body protesting about its sudden encasement. Worse still had been the glamorous softly-boned basque that Tuppy had also lavished upon her. Truly it had turned what she had always assumed to be an average figure into something much more remarkable . . . but at the loss of a great deal of personal comfort! Tuppy in her job as a top-flight demonstrator was used to wearing such confining garments. She, Penny, certainly was not! So when discomfort changed to pain she had sneaked upstairs at the party, found an empty bedroom and stripped off both the dress and the offending basque beneath it. Her plan had been to unpick the seams of the undergarment and remove the rigid stays which were bruising her ribs.

Just as she had laid the satin and lace undergarment down on the bed beside her dress and was heaving in the first really deep breath she'd been able to take that afternoon, Saul had burst into the room and discovered her . . .

'Then the display of female pulchritude was meant for my eyes, was it?' A cynical smile deepened the grooves down his cheeks, but his eyes were cold. 'My dear Penny! You should have warned me. After all, it was purely an accident that someone spilled tomato sauce over my shirt and I had to come up and change. I'd no idea what you'd planned!'

She drew in a breath in an effort to keep control of her temper. That his arrival had been totally unforeseen by either of them illustrated clearly the facetiousness of his suggestion and didn't merit a denial. Instead she told him acidly, 'If you'd been a gentleman you'd have gone straight out when . . .'

'When I went into my own bedroom in my own house and found a naked woman sitting on my bed . . . warm and willing?'

'I wasn't naked!' It was a cry of desperation. And she hadn't been warm or willing either. Just horribly embarrassed, as after one all-consuming appraisal of her rigid body, Saul had turned his back on her and begun to strip off first his jacket, then his shirt, exposing a firmly muscled back to her petrified stare.

She had sat tongue-tied while he re-dressed with lazy efficiency. Somewhere there had been the right words to explain her presence and appearance, but in that moment of deep humiliation she had been unable to find them, sitting in silent agony as Saul finished changing and with one last scornful look had left her close to tears.

'No, you weren't, were you?' His smile deepened reminiscently as his fingers moved in an insolent caress of her shoulders. 'As I recall it you were very provocatively "half-naked".' Formidable eyes drifted over her taut body as goose-pimples formed in the wake of their mocking scrutiny. 'What is it with women like you? Beautiful ... desirable ...' His contemptuous glance removed any compliment from the adjectives. 'Isn't ordinary sex good enough for you? Do you always have to look for new experiences? Does the thrill of imminent discovery really make it *that* good?'

A wave of sickness engulfed her. If she'd had any idea Saul had brooded over the incident and found his own cruel interpretation of such an innocent action, she would never have come to him. Never!

'Stop it! You don't understand!'

'Understand? Oh, I understand very well when I walk into a bedroom and find a woman posed on a bed like an odalisque from some Turkish seraglio awaiting the Sultan's pleasure ... all opulent breasts and silky thighs ... Tell me,' his voice deepened as he ignored her trembling outrage, making no attempt to conceal the curiosity in his grey eyes, 'which one of the guests at your goddaughter's christening was the lucky guy?'

He had gone too far, the hateful smile that parted his lips was more than she could bear. With a muted cry Penny swung her arm back, intent on striking his lean cheek with all the force at her command.

Instead, she found her wrist imprisoned in an iron grasp as the smile died an instant death.

'And if you won't answer that question ... here's another one. Why haven't you been to him with your infamous suggestion? Is he already married? Isn't he rich enough to support you and Lucy in the lifestyle you're looking for ... or has he disappeared from your life?'

'Let me go, you brute!' Fiercely Penny tried to release her wrist, determined now not to dignify his obscene questions with an answer. 'I should have never come here!'

Saul didn't deny it. Instead he pulled her hard against him, using his free arm to encircle her waist.

'Just one more thing before you leave.' His voice, deep and meaningful, forced itself through her dazed understanding. 'If you want a baby so badly there are more pleasurable ways of obtaining one than by trying to corrupt a court of law with your lies.'

She knew what was coming—and was powerless to avoid it, as Saul lowered his dark head to possess her mouth with brutal thoroughness.

Automatically she raised her hands to reject him, feeling his muscles flex beneath the fine cotton of his shirt as she touched him. She was so close she could feel the heavy hammer of his heart against her own soft breasts, the tension in his powerful body as he raped her unwilling mouth. Her legs went weak, she was suffocating, a deep moan echoed in the air-starved column of her throat ... and she was released, thrust away from him, gasping and shaken.

Somehow she found her coat and got it on over her shaking shoulders. Blindly she made for the door, hearing Saul's heavy breathing, aware that he was watching her, enjoying her reaction to the humiliation he had inflicted on her.

As her fingers gripped the handle that led to freedom, somehow she summoned up the last dregs of her fighting spirit.

'I wish it had been you who'd gone to Mexico and not Michael!'

She didn't wait to see his expression, hurling the words at random into the room.

Letting herself out of the office, she bestowed an insincere smile on the receptionist. At least, she comforted herself, the walls were thick; her exchange of hostilities with the brute who owned the van Diemen Consultancy wouldn't have been overheard by his staff.

She managed to maintain her composure until she was well away from the building. Only then did she acknowledge her defeat and allow herself the luxury of tears.

CHAPTER THREE

OF COURSE she had always known she was leaving herself open to humiliation. It had been the price she had been prepared to pay for the satisfaction of knowing she had exhausted every possibility of presenting herself in the best possible light to the authorities.

Last night in bed it had seemed such a wonderful solution to contract a temporary 'paper' marriage, and she had embraced it with a vibrant optimism, only to see it cruelly and systematically destroyed by a salvo of unmerited ammunition!

Saul van Diemen—'Huh!' The girl behind the counter of the coffee bar where she'd gone for sustenance gave Penny a startled look as she breathed her contempt aloud.

Deep in her own thoughts, Penny was unaware that her despair had been observed. How dared the autocratic man her sister and brother-in-law had chosen to be their daughter's godfather think for one second that she would have gone to him for help if there'd been anyone else she could have turned to!

The sad fact was that, far from her living the Bohemian life he had imagined, most of her time was spent in the close confines of her own small flat working at the glass engraving which, in time, would bring her a healthy income, but which, at the moment, was bringing in only enough to keep her head above water.

It wasn't an occupation where one was likely to meet

eligible men, she reflected morosely. Not that she'd seen
that as a disadvantage until the Mexican tragedy and the
sudden realisation that she would have had a much better
chance of claiming guardianship for her orphaned niece
if she had been able to produce a husband and stable
background.

In a year she would be successful enough in her own
right to substantiate the quality of her claim. But in a
year's time Lucy could be beyond her reach . . . besides,
she didn't want to miss another day of the little girl's life.

So, reason had told her, it had to be Saul van Diemen.
It had been a hard decision to make. The fact that Saul
had caught her in such an embarrassing predicament had
still rankled. It had been the reason she had refused his
previous offer of help, preferring to obtain her own
solicitor rather than be forced into his company again.
For Lucy's sake she had swallowed her pride. After all,
she'd told herself dourly, the shock he had suffered on
seeing her could hardly have surpassed her own as he had
erupted unexpectedly into her presence! She had never
imagined he had put such a sinister meaning to her
impromptu striptease—or that his opinion of her had
remained so abysmally low.

Dear God, this was the man her twin sister had cared
enough for to enjoy a brief affair with! She had expected
him to have some redeeming features. Even though she
and Tuppy had been fraternal, not identical twins and
had therefore borne no more physical resemblance to
each other than any two sisters in one family, they had
been very close to each other, sharing common tastes and
interests. A faint smile disturbed the solemnity of her
pale face. Although Tuppy had always been the more
extrovert by nature, she had never been the empty-

headed glamour girl she had mischievously emulated from time to time. Her pre-motherhood job as a demonstrator had demanded a high degree of intelligence and application as well as glamour! Fiercely Penny championed her sister's memory before sighing and rising to her feet.

Probably Tuppy had discovered that the promise of Saul's handsome face and strong, lithe male body wasn't carried out in his character. No doubt her sister had found him vain and narrow-minded with no sense of fair play, and that was why she had chosen to marry the kinder, more considerate Michael. Yet there must have been some lingering pleasant memories, or else why would she have nominated Saul to play what should have been such an important role in Lucy's life?

Penny closed the door of the café behind her, and started walking towards the London Underground sign she could see in the distance. Once on the system she could find her way to the main line station where she could catch a train back to the suburbs.

Wearily she pushed her fingers through her wealth of deep auburn hair, feeling the tangle of curls intensified by the atmosphere. Already she had spent too much time walking through the damp city streets indulging her misery before stopping for refreshment. It was time to go home to Lucy.

If no one would help her, then she'd fight on alone. The strongest point in her favour was that Lucy's parents had entrusted their child to her sole care when they went abroad. It demonstrated their faith in her.

She hoped it would be enough. Because now Saul had refused her any support she had nothing else in her favour. Nothing at all.

Two hours later she was turning the corner into the
short cul-de-sac where the Stanleys' three-bedroomed
semi was located. In the past days Margaret Stanley, who
knew the whole tragic background of Lucy's predicament, had become a good friend, welcoming her charge's
young aunt into her house at any time.

In her mid-forties, Margaret exuded an air of
competency and genuine affection. From the first
moment she had met the woman who had been
appointed Lucy's short-term foster-mother, Penny felt a
great weight lifted from her mind. For the time being she
was content that Lucy was happy and thriving. It was her
only consolation.

In answer to her knock Margaret greeted Penny at the
front door with a beaming smile, waving her into the
main sitting-room.

'Go straight in, dear. I was just going to put her
upstairs to bed, but I got a bit delayed, so I'm finishing
the dinner preparations for the rest of the family first.'

'Fine!' Penny smiled her thanks, pushing the door
open and taking a couple of steps into the room, her lips
poised to respond to Lucy's customary gurgle of greeting.
In the next instant she came to an abrupt halt as her legs
turned to jelly and the blood drummed painfully in her
ears.

'You'll forgive me if I don't get up.' The voice she had
hoped never to hear again drawled his excuse as Saul's
right hand indicated the cuddlesome bundle in the pink
pyjama-grow which nestled lovingly on his lap, her back
supported by his left arm.

Lucy smiled her enchanting two-toothed smile into
Penny's eyes, holding out her arms delightedly. Somehow Penny found the strength to cross the room towards

her, bending to kiss the satin cheek. She was delicious, her silky black hair framing her magnolia skin, her blue eyes so like her mother's enormous in her chubby face as she cooed her pleasure.

With the sweet smell of baby powder fresh in her nostrils Penny stepped back to glower down upon Saul's bland face.

'What do you think you're doing here!' she demanded tersely, her mind spinning with the improbability of his presence. 'How did you know where to come? What do you want?' The constriction in her throat made her tones strangled as fear tautened her muscles. Convinced his being there must pose trouble for her, she stared at him with anguished eyes.

'I'm visiting my godchild.' His calmness taunted her uncertainty with a cruel satisfaction. 'It seemed a reasonable thing to do in the circumstatnces. And as to how I knew where to come—after the information you gave me, belated though it was, my solicitors had no trouble in tracing Lucy's whereabouts.' He removed one of the baby's probing fingers from an exploration of his ear, kissed it absent-mindedly before imprisoning it playfully in one of his large capable hands.

Penny looked from the spatulate fingers with their neatly manicured nails back to his personable face. Light eyes broody behind the masking wedge of lashes met her own with enigmatic coolness.

She must be lightheaded from lack of food, because at that instant she had a vivid mental picture of herself in the role of Little Red Riding Hood having gone into the wood to ask the Wolf for help.

'How did you know I'd be here?' she demanded imperiously.

Strong shoulders moved negligently. 'I didn't come here to see you. I came to see Lucy.' There was a short pause while Penny struggled to keep calm. 'Your turn was coming later, my love.'

The endearment was contemptuous, the statement bearing all the hallmarks of a threat. She shivered uncontrollably. He still hadn't answered all her questions.

'What do you want?' she asked again through clenched teeth.

'To honour my obligations.' Diemen by name and demon by nature, she thought, his smile was angelic as his arm tightened round Lucy's soft suit. 'What else did you expect?' Whatever it was it certainly hadn't been this prompt and unwelcome visitation!

She was saved from the necessity of answering by Margaret Stanley re-entering the room. As Saul hoisted his godchild firmly to rest against his shoulder and rose to his full height, turning his suave expression towards Lucy's foster-mother, Penny was unbearably reminded of the terrifying moment at the church ceremony when the unaccustomed tightness round her diaphragm had caused her to come over faint. Saul had come instantly and fortuitously to her rescue, taking Lucy from her shaking arms and supporting her own swaying body with the steel girder of his arm.

Perhaps that incident had been the birthpoint of his contempt for her, she accorded with a flash of insight. Certainly the look he had given her had been censorious rather than sympathetic, as if she had been unaware of how horrific the consequences of falling with Lucy in her arms might have been to her young charge. How glad she was that Tuppy had never found out how disastrous her loving attempts to glamorise her sister in her own image had turned out to be!

Forcing a smile to her face, she suddenly realised Margaret's pleasant countenance was glowing with excitement.

'I couldn't be happier for you, my dear!' The older woman stepped forward to hug her, pressing her cheek against Penny's in a gesture of spontaneous joy. 'You deserve all the happiness you can get!' She stood back, her face alight with pleasure. 'I could have cried when Mr van Diemen introduced himself to me and told me your plans.'

'But I didn't . . . I couldn't . . . what plans?' She hadn't felt as weak as this since she'd caught 'flu. Please God she wasn't going to suffer a relapse! Helplessly she stared at Margaret as the older woman continued to smile at her.

'Our plans to get married and give Lucy a home, of course, darling.' Saul bestowed a condescendingly gentle look on her dazed face as she turned to meet his deeply voiced avowal.

A taste as bitter as gall sullied her burning throat as she gazed into his unrelenting smile. Not content with what he'd already done, he'd dared to come here to mock her in front of the only friend and ally she had?

'No!' she gasped the word, rejecting whatever further cruelty he had in store for her, flinching as she saw Margaret's pleasant face cloud with concern at the harshness of her denial. She swallowed miserably. Everything she said was making matters worse. Turning hunted eyes towards her tormentor, she held out her arms. 'Please . . . I want to hold her.'

'Of course.'

Saul handed the child to her, but having made the exchange, remained close, supporting her trembling body with one firm arm. 'I suggest you see her safely tucked up for the night, my love, and then the two of us will go out, have some dinner and discuss our plans in detail.'

It sounded such a reasonable suggestion that to contest it openly would make her appear mad. Whatever Saul's game was, she would rather it was played out without an audience. She wouldn't go out with him, and she wouldn't eat with him: but if the only way to get him out of this house was to say she would—then so be it.

Without a word she accepted Margaret's silent indication to perform the bedtime honours and left the room, hugging the warm little body to her heart.

'I passed a very pleasant-looking restaurant on my way here—restored Tudor, by the look of it—standing back from the road in its own grounds.'

Penny turned slightly to regard the firm profile of the man whose competent hands on the wheel of the Jaguar XJS were guiding them inexorably towards the Olde Manor Farm. Trust Saul van Diemen to home in on the county's most renowned and expensive restaurant! By repute it was luxurious, spacious and discreet, while the quality of its food won it many stars in gourmet guides to good eating.

'I'm not dressed for such opulence,' she returned stiffly. 'And I'm not hungry either.'

She'd got into his car because it would have been childish to refuse his offer of a lift, especially as she felt so drained of energy. However, she had asked him to drive her home . . . not out on the town! Thank heavens some element of self-preservation had stimulated her into freshening herself up and re-applying her basic make-up after she had kissed Lucy goodnight. If Saul insisted on taking her to the Olde Manor Farm at least she'd look clean if nothing else—and from the stubborn set of his chin and the dominant glint in his grey eyes she was receiving very strong messages that the autocratic male beside her intended to have his own way.

'Had a good lunch, did you?' he enquired pleasantly, not taking his gaze from the road. 'It may surprise you to know I didn't.' He cornered the powerful car with a skill its elegant design deserved. 'As a matter of fact, after you left I cancelled my lunch engagement and stayed in the office to clear up some necessary work before coming over here.'

Penny sighed. 'That was your fault, not mine. I didn't ask you to come.'

'No,' he agreed quietly, steering the car between the great oak posts that marked the boundary of the restaurant's grounds and bringing it round to park neatly by the entrance. Penny was still fumbling with the clasp of her seat-belt seconds later as he stood patiently holding open the passenger door for her to alight. The hand that assisted her didn't release its positive grip on her arm. 'No, Penny,' he repeated, his lean face harsh and unsmiling. 'But you did ask me to marry you. And that is exactly what I mean to do.'

She'd thought he was having a cruel joke at her expense in front of Margaret, but there was no sign of amusement in his brooding expression now.

'But . . .' There were no words to express her horror. She had just spent the last hours castigating her own stupidity in believing she could have ever lived under the same roof as this man in any circumstances . . . and now this!

'Don't argue with me, Penny. I'm not in the mood for it,' he warned swiftly. 'We've a great deal to discuss, and we're going to do it now, tonight, over a good meal.'

For the space of three seconds she actually considered defying him before deciding against it. Apart from the fact that it would be a long lonely walk back to her flat, the firm hands on her arms suggested a silent promise of physical persuasion if she disobeyed him, and if she was going into the restaurant she'd rather walk than be carried.

As far as the décor was concerned the Olde Manor Farm merited its acclaim, she decided. The table they had been shown to with its linen cloth, silver cutlery and sparkling crystal was ideally situated in a corner of the spacious, candlelit room. Thick carpet, sumptuous seating and a background of light orchestral music were an immediate balm to her raw nerves. Curiously she touched the single deep red rosebud in the silver specimen vase in front of her. It was real. The last rose of summer, she thought a trifle hysterically as she waved away Saul's offer of the menu with an abrupt gesture.

'I told you I'm not hungry.'

'Well, I am.' With a sharp lift of his head he summoned the hovering waiter to his side. 'Melon followed by Sole Véronique, I think. Make that twice. And a bottle of Chablis Premier Cru to accompany it.'

'I said I wasn't hungry!' Penny burst out, her eyes sparkling with temper as the waiter's back receded from them. Damn Saul van Diemen! Was he determined to force food down her as well as his decisions? And surely he couldn't really intend to agree with her proposition after all he'd said?

'Then leave it,' he instructed coldly. 'If you don't care for it you should have made your own selection when I asked you to; but I don't intend to have you sitting there with an empty plate in front of you like a sulky child.'

'I'm wondering just what you do intend!' she returned tightly, knowing full well she wouldn't be able to resist the light yet delicious meal he had ordered on her behalf. Already her dormant taste buds were awakening—a fact she resented enormously. She wanted nothing from him now—especially anything that would bring her enjoyment.

'I told you, I intend to accept your proposal of marriage.'

'After the way you turned the idea down?' Her voice was loaded with sarcasm. 'Do you take me for a fool?'

'A fool? No. Foolish, yes.' Saul paused as the wine waiter approached to go through the tradition of approving first the label and then the sample measure poured for his approbation, continuing smoothly when they were alone, 'If you assume the right to propose marriage to me, then surely I have the right to change my mind?'

'A right I can't see you exercising on many occasions.' Penny made no attempt to hide her dislike of him. 'You seem to be naturally obstinate and intractable.'

Annoyingly, he didn't seem upset by her condemnation. To her chagrin he even managed a smile—a movement that robbed his perfectly formed mouth of the chiselled petulance of a Greek God it had in repose and lent his strong-boned face a devastating attractiveness. Disconcertingly Penny felt a slow warm blush crawl the length of her body, and wondered if this was the kind of effect he had had on Tuppy. Resolutely she stared at the spotless tablecloth as his calm voice passed over her bent head. 'Personally I prefer to call myself positive and determined, but I'm not going to fight with you over adjectives.'

There was another enforced silence as the waiter placed half on Ogen melon in front of each of them.

'Of course,' Saul continued equably after his departure, 'there will have to be a change in your original plan.'

Her hand tightening round the spoon she had automatically lifted, Penny met his commanding eyes with a feeling of utter despair. 'What change?'

'The new deal is a normal marriage between us, with no previous understanding about annulment or divorce.'

CHAPTER FOUR

HOLDING her breath in consternation, Penny stared at Saul's provocative face, aware of the glittering challenge behind his cool gaze. How could he possibly want to tie them together for life when he'd already castigated her as immoral and venal?

'Are you serious?' She gasped the words out in a breathy rush that emphasised her amazement.

'Deadly so.' The smile he flashed held no humour. 'After you left this morning I began to see the power of your argument. When I agreed to be Lucy's godfather I *did* accept a moral responsibility for her future—one which I'm now prepared to honour—especially as you made the point so dramatically that I'm initially responsible for her parents' death.'

The flicker of pain crossing his face wasn't assumed. Seeing it, Penny felt a pang of remorse at her specious accusation.

'Consequently,' Saul continued evenly, 'I've decided to provide a permanent home for her. Since I have no recognised relationship with her it follows that my only course is to accept your proposal and support your claim. It's as simple as that.'

'But you despise me! How can you possibly contemplate a permanent relationship between us?' In her agitation Penny dug her spoon into the melon, scooping out the soft flesh and transferring it to her mouth. Cool and fragrant, it pleasured her taste buds, but she was scarcely aware of it.

Saul was holding out a lifeline to her—but at what

cost! She had envisaged a temporary imprisonment under the aegis of his power—not a life sentence!

'Why not?' His casual answer made no attempt to deny her estimation of his feelings. 'I *do* need a housekeeper.' He moved his broad shoulders deprecatingly. 'I was living in a service flat in London when I discovered that house and fell in love with it at first sight. On the spur of the moment I bought it.' A wry self-mocking smile brought a sudden softness to his lean face. 'Like all decisions based on emotion rather than logic, it was a disaster. During my absence on business it's neglected, uninhabited, open to damage by bad weather or vandals. It isn't aired enough in summer or heated enough in winter. I've lived there for a year, but it still has an alien feel about it. It's never given me the welcome and comfort I wanted from it.' The mocking inflection that had coloured his tone deepened. 'It's like a woman who resents the lack of attention she considers her due. It freezes me out.'

'An interesting comparison,' said Penny cautiously. She might not personally find him irresistible, but it was difficult to imagine any woman in whom Saul van Diemen showed an interest freezing him out. Some deep feminine instinct told her that the man regarding her with a cynical twist on his lips could be successfully persuasive with most members of the female sex if and when the fancy took him. Even her own sister had succumbed to his wiles for a short time before she'd settled for the quieter, gentler Michael . . .

Aware that he was watching her face with every sign of amusement, she tore her thoughts away from his unsavoury personal life. 'I imagine any efficient house-keeper could bring it the warmth you require.'

'Contradicting your own argument?' Dark brows teased her. 'Since Michael appears to have discussed my affairs with you at some length, it's obvious you know the difficulties I've experienced in trying to find anyone remotely suitable.' His gaze grew thoughtful, evaluating her pale face. 'I've decided a wife would be a more realiable appointment—but not on any temporary basis.'

Conscious of his eyes pinned on her soft mouth as she stoically ate her melon, Penny listened without comment. His voice, soft yet businesslike, continued.

'You made the point yourself. It's a very large house with ample accommodation—certainly enough to allow you to have your own bedroom as well as a separate nursery for Lucy.'

Penny stirred uncomfortably as he paused. It seemed this unknown package of arrant masculinity, this urban lion in the guise of a civilised business man, having been made aware of his obligations, didn't intend to rest until he'd discharged them—and it was his plan to make her pay an apt penalty for daring to have pointed them out to him in the first place.

At least, she thought with a little shudder, he wasn't suggesting they should co-habit as man and wife. He had promised her her own bedroom—but even then—no, it was too much to ask of her.

'I could never consider a permanent relationship with you,' she told him quietly. 'It was never my intention to enter into anything but a temporary business arrangement, as I explained.'

Saul's eyes narrowed thoughtfully as he watched the downcast head before him, long lashes casting a shadow on cheeks which showed too clearly the high flaring bones beneath their pale skin, the soft mouth whose fresh pinkness owed nothing to make-up. He ran his hand through his own dark hair with a gesture of angry impatience.

'Then you have to consider saying goodbye to Lucy, because I could never settle for your terms!' He leaned forward across the table, his tone vibrant with anger. 'Until you appeared in my office this morning I'd no idea of the situation you'd floundered into. I'd naturally assumed, from your reaction to my offer of help earlier, that you'd put yourself and Lucy under someone else's "patronage".' Penny couldn't miss the sardonic gleam in those grey eyes as he flung her own descriptive word back at her. 'And frankly I find your bravado foolhardy rather than commendable!' Scathingly he regarded her above the table-linen. 'My God, woman, when did you last have a square meal? You're not fit to look after yourself, let alone a dependent child, without supervision!'

'I was ill . . .!' she lashed back fierily, stung to defend herself from the assault of his astringent accusation.

'And will be again if you carry on like this.' There was no pity on his face as he cut across her sentence, only a fierce intensity of purpose. 'If I'd realised at the time what you intended to do I'd have acted sooner.'

'By asking me to marry you?' she enquired with a sweet sarcasm as her stormy eyes met his steady gaze.

'By making Lucy a ward of court.'

'No!' It was a cry of pain, muted because of propriety, but straight from her heart. It hadn't been an idle threat, she knew. Anyone could make a minor a ward of court if he or she suspected neglect. She swallowed rapidly, terrified by the power of his antagonism across the table from her. Dear God, what had she got herself into?

She raised her head proudly but couldn't disguise the translucent shimmer of tears that made her eyes sparkle. 'Are you threatening to oppose my application for guardianship unless I agree to marry you on your terms?' Each word was like a self-inflicted stab wound.

'I shan't need to.' Saul's mouth tightened ominously. 'You outlined the problems to me yourself. All of them except one . . .'

Dark eyebrows invited her comment, but Penny was too frozen to respond, only her eyes like two dark bruises in her pale face told Saul he had her entire attention.

'I had my solicitor check up on the lease of your flat after you left me. It seems you're infringing your tenancy agreement by running a business there. Once your background comes under scrutiny your business will have to close down. Either that or you'll be out on the street without a roof over your head.'

Across the table his gaze held her own with no trace of pity in its cool perception.

'I can't see Lucy being allowed to share that fate, can you?'

Pain seared through Penny as she felt the blood leave her face. Blindly she reached for her glass. Lifting it with a hand that shook, she took a deep draught of the dry, lightly scented white wine. Desperately her tortured mind sought an answer . . . and found none.

'Well?'

The terse question pierced her reverie, to be followed by a softer tone as Saul asked emotively, 'What's it to be? Care . . . or custody?'

'After what you said to me this morning?' Her eyes were bitter as she stared back at him.

'So I bruised your pride a little. Are you going to let that stand in your way?'

Not only my pride, she thought rebelliously. Her lips still remembered the violence of his mouth, the contemptuous way he had chosen to demonstrate his opinion of her.

Her troubled eyes rose to search his face, dwelling on the luminous dilated pupils that seemed to bore into her soul, their silvered outer rim making his steady gaze compelling. Saul was a passionate, sensual man. She hadn't needed the cold brutality of his kiss to tell her that.

Everything about him suggested his underlying sexuality. She wasn't stupid or prudish enough to assume he intended becoming celibate simply because theirs was to be a convenient union without consummation. But didn't men have a need to fulfil themselves as much as women . . . to found their own dynasties?

Undoubtedly Saul would take lovers, but did he really mean to deny himself the joy of fathering his own legitimate children? Or hadn't he even considered that element of the arrangement he was suggesting?

'Suppose we should fall in love?' she asked at last in a small voice.

For a moment it seemed he wasn't going to answer. When he did speak his voice was crisp.

'Love is for the young and innocent, a fantasy for adolescents. I've lived through the disintegration of a marriage contracted when I was young enough to believe there was more to a relationship with a woman than the satisfaction of physical desire . . .'

Mesmerised by the pain evident in his clear light eyes, Penny felt an instinctive wave of sympathy as he paused. She didn't know what went on inside that dark head, behind those enigmatic eyes. If she agreed to marry him she would have to guess at his moods, anticipate his needs, but she would never grow close to him, understand him, share his life in the way she had always hoped to with the man she married . . .

'And you,' he said softly, leaning across the table towards her. 'I'm sure you, too, have learned that what we call "love" is a transient pleasure, hmm?'

As the image of herself perched on his bed in semi-nudity sprang to her mind, Penny felt her face flood with warm colour, 'I think I ought to explain . . .' she began earnestly, only to be silenced as he reached towards her, covering her hand with his own.

'No, Penny—no explanations, please. Whatever you did before we met is no concern of mine. It's the future that matters.' He smiled without rancour. 'At least a marriage arranged without the complications of false emotions should be less traumatic for both of us. You'll meet my conditions gracefully and without argument because it will be in your interests to keep my goodwill. And in return I shall be grateful to enjoy a life of harmony free from the recriminations that destroy so many so-called "love matches" when the first halcyon days are over.'

It was so nearly the solution she'd sought: the answer Saul had denied her earlier that day. Penny swallowed painfully. Why did it suddenly seem so cold-blooded and sordid?

She knew Saul was watching her, his dark brows drawn together in a frown of impatience.

'Make your mind up, Penny.' His terse instruction demanded her decision. 'It's a long-term marriage—or nothing. I won't lend my name or my reputation to deceive the court. If Lucy comes under my roof now, she stays there until she comes of age.'

With agonised eyes she met his stern regard. Would she be able to live in any kind of harmony with this dynamic man whose determined chin and steely gaze insisted on her compliance with his plan? She didn't know. One thing she did know, though—if she were to lose custody of Lucy through her own selfishness she wouldn't be able to live with herself.

'Very well.' Lips parched, her throat burning, she managed to utter the words. 'I accept your terms.'

'Good.' There was no emotion in the level voice that accepted her surrender. It was as if he'd always known he held the whip hand, Penny thought with a shudder. 'You'd better wear this for appearances' sake.'

A small box was pushed across the table towards her. Intrigued, eyes widening in amazement, she stared down at the half-circle of crossed sapphires and diamonds.

'To match your eyes—sapphires for their colour, diamonds for their sparkle when you get angry.' For the first time there was a hint of intimacy in his husky drawl: a suggestion of amusement that made her skin crawl.

Flushing beneath what she defined as mockery, Penny slipped the ring on her finger. Doubtless there would be instances ahead where she would have to oppose him. A sixth sense warned her that it would be in her own interests to keep such confrontations to a minimum.

To her surprise the ring fitted perfectly.

'Like Cinderella's slipper,' murmured Saul, reading her astonishment. 'Not so incredible really. I particularly noticed your slender fingers when we first met.'

'Oh!' Ignominy brought a cry of resentment to her soft lips. How could he remind her of that shameful incident when she'd desperately tried to mask her near-nakedness with her hands? Especially when he had just pre-empted her attempt to explain the circumstances—not that he would have believed them anyway . . . for some reason she'd become his 'dog with a bad name' and he was determined to hang her one way or the other!

Her reproachful expression brought a low laugh from Saul's throat as his mouth twisted in a faint sardonic smile. 'When you were showing me the bowl you'd engraved for Lucy—remember?'

Before she had regained her composure his face had resumed the businesslike severity to which she had grown accustomed. 'Do you have a passport?'

The sudden change of subject made her blink. 'No. I've never been abroad.'

'Well, no matter. It's easily arranged.'

Casually he dismissed the matter, settling himself

more comfortably in his chair. How much more relaxed he was, Penny realised suddenly. It seemed that once Saul had made up his mind he had been resolved on the outcome. The announcement in front of Margaret, the purchase of an engagement ring ... Now the hard edge of ruthlessness she had been aware of from their first meeting seemed dulled. In victory it appeared he was prepared to be generous.

'We're going abroad?' she hazarded. Her life was changing with such rapidity she could have been dreaming.

'Paris, for a couple of days.' Succinctly she received her answer. 'We can marry with a special licence by the middle of next week when I have a vital business meeting there.' The brisk efficiency in his tone intensified. 'You can leave all the arrangements to me. It will suit me very well to take a wife to Paris.'

There was a sudden insolence in the assessing gaze he raked over her that made Penny's heart rate increase alarmingly, as he finished his observation in a lazy drawl.

'Now, I suggest you finish your dinner before it spoils. Skinny women have never been to my taste.'

Penny obeyed the terse instruction. Like a condemned criminal enjoying a last meal before execution she finished the fish, following it with strawberries and cream. With a strangely revitalised appetite she even managed to nibble her way through several petits fours which were served with the coffee.

It wasn't until she was seated beside Saul once more in the Jaguar, having given him instructions for reaching the small block of flats where she lived, that he mentioned the subject of the wedding ceremony.

'I assume your local registrar's office is a satisfactory venue for the proceedings?' he queried, his gaze intent on the road ahead.

Penny nodded, then, aware he wasn't looking at her, put her thought into words. 'Well, a church would be a bit of a mockery, wouldn't it? All those promises about loving and honouring?' Not to mention the vows . . . 'with my body I thee worship', she added silently to herself, suppressing the shiver that trembled through her body at the thought of Saul's very masculine body in close contact with her own—let alone worshipping it!

He shot her a quick sideways glance. 'I dare say people have married in church for far less honourable motives than our own,' he said drily. 'But I agree, a civil ceremony is preferable. Do you want to invite guests?'

The question took her by surprise. 'Oh—no, I don't think so.' One of her closest friends had emigrated, the other was in hospital expecting her first baby. And, of course, she had no family or she wouldn't have been forced into this invidious position in the first place!

'It's a mockery you'd prefer your friends not to witness, hm?' A hard edge of anger toughened Saul's voice as he broke across her sentence.

Penny felt the rebuke as if he'd slapped her. 'You seem to forget I'm in mourning,' she riposted tartly, unwilling to reveal how small her circle of friends was. 'I prefer to keep it quiet . . . although it would be nice to have Margaret Stanley there . . . with Lucy.'

She looked at the hard profile turned towards her. 'Naturally I would expect you to invite some of your family,' she added primly.

'Then don't.' The abruptness of the reply startled her. 'I have no one I care for. By all means invite Margaret . . . the registrar can supply the other witness.'

Silenced by the asperity in his tone, Penny merely inclined her head. After all, there was no reason why Saul would want personal witnesses to the loveless union she'd forced on him through the agency of his own pride, was there?

How different Tuppy's wedding had been, she mused as the car sped on its way. That too had been a civil ceremony held in the London district where her sister had been living so that she could be close to the hotels and exhibition halls where she'd worked as a demonstrator before Lucy's birth.

Already nearly five months pregnant, Tuppy had been a radiant bride, flamboyantly beautiful in coral silk, her flaming red hair, several shades brighter than Penny's own, a glowing mantle on her slim shoulders.

For a long time Tuppy had insisted that marriage wasn't for her: that she was quite capable of having and looking after her own child without tying herself down. When she had finally changed her mind, with typical bravura she had thrown an enormous party to celebrate. Of all their friends and acquaintances only Saul had been missing. She remembered Tuppy telling her with awe about the generous cheque Michael's boss had given them. 'I'd so wanted you to meet him,' her sister had sighed, 'but he's in the Middle East on business.'

'There you are—that's it.' Penny broke into her own memories to touch Saul's arm lightly, indicating that they had arrived at their destination.

'I'll see you to your front door,' he declared brusquely, waving away her half-hearted protest and following her through the main entrance. Three flights later he took her key from her hand, opening the door for her, then stepping back.

'Do you want to come in?' Proudly she turned on the threshold, sure he wouldn't miss an opportunity of seeing the conditions in which she lived.

Plainly furnished it might be, small and overcrowded with Lucy's bits and pieces it certainly was, but it was neat and clean and she refused to be ashamed of it.

'No.' Saul shook his dark head. 'It's late and you need your sleep.'

His half-closed lids gave him a sultry look, and for the first time that evening Penny saw the lines of strain apparent on his handsome face and felt a surge of pity for him. This coming marriage was as unwelcome to him as it was to her and was obviously giving him a similar mental grief.

She stifled a yawn, grateful for his unexpected consideration. 'I *am* very tired,' she agreed tonelessly.

'I'll let you know the exact arrangements and get someone to come round and help you pack the things you want to bring with you to your new home.'

'Yes, thank you. Is that all?' Her blue eyes, heavy with resignation and weariness, sought his answer, turning their heavy-lashed beauty to dwell on the face of the stranger she was about to commit her life to.

'Not quite.'

She was too physically tired and emotionally weary to struggle as Saul caught her close. Her mouth trembled as he lowered his dark head, fearful of a further harsh assault that would reinforce his contempt and reassert the mastery he could exert over her to ensure her obedience if he so chose.

Instead he touched her with a light caress, trailing hard, silky lips gently across her vulnerable mouth. It was an undemanding salute, ending when he left her mouth to touch her forehead with the same fleeting caress, leaving her breathless and bewildered until he spoke.

'We don't have to love each other, Penny . . . but we do have to be friends or we're about to do Lucy an appalling injustice. Unless, together, we can give her a home she's going to be happy in, a place of concord to which she can invite her friends with confidence, we'd do better to call this whole thing off now. Do you understand what I'm saying?'

Dumbly she nodded her russet head. In his own way Saul was asking her forgiveness for his harsh attitude towards her, guaranteeing not to hold what he saw as he murky past against her, offering her a fresh start.

For one mad moment she had an impulse to insist on telling him how badly he had misunderstood the bizarre incident at Lucy's christening. But then why should he believe her? It was more dignified to leave matters as they stood.

'I'll be in touch, then.' Correctly reading her silence as acceptance of his truce, Saul turned away.

Slowly Penny closed the door, making her way towards her bedroom. Pausing to rest her hands on Lucy's empty cot, she drifted her gaze from the vacant bed to the sparkling jewel on her finger.

'Please God,' she prayed with painful intensity, 'let me be doing the right thing.'

CHAPTER FIVE

EIGHT days later Penelope Kingston held out a steady hand to receive the gold band that would confirm her new status as Mrs Saul van Diemen.

In a pleasant room where the scent of pot-grown cyclamen and garden chrysanthemums mingled into an exotic fragrance she signed her maiden name for the last time in the register, watched by a broadly beaming Lucy, safely clasped in Margaret Stanley's arms.

Wiping away a surreptitious tear as Penny laid down the pen, the latter demanded tartly of Saul, 'Well, aren't you going to kiss the bride?'

'Of course.' Smilingly he obeyed the command, depositing a firm caress on Penny's delicately coloured mouth.

She accepted the salutation stoically. Since Saul had made it clear he wanted their marriage to appear normal, she would have to get used to the rare demonstration of this kind, she supposed: and really she had no objection to his attentions at this perfunctory level. He was, after all, a very attractive man whose nearness was not at all unpleasant. Today particularly in a silver-grey suit superbly tailored to his tall well-formed male body, he was little short of magnificent, she admitted.

'Well, I suppose that will have to suffice until you get some privacy.' Margaret gave Penny a hug with one arm, offering Lucy to her with the other. 'Here, my poppet— kiss your Auntie Penny goodbye. She's going on a lovely honeymoon with her gorgeous new husband—and who's going to go and live with them when they come back?' She handed the still beaming Lucy over into Penny's keeping before turning towards the patiently waiting Saul.

As Penny cuddled her niece with a fierce love, her eyes filled with laughter at Lucy's enormous toothy grin, she could hear Margaret speaking to Saul.

'All my congratulations, Mr van Diemen. You've won yourself a very lovely lady there. Not only in looks . . .' she passed an appreciative eye over Penny's white silk chiffon dress '. . . but in character too . . . as I'm sure you know.'

'Yes, indeed.' Saul's silky smooth tone drew Penny's attention, and she turned to see his mouth curved into a wicked smile. 'She's a very determined lady when she really wants something . . . aren't you, my darling?'

'I fight for what I want, yes . . .' She spared him an anxious look, aware of the undertone to the question and not sure how to take his half mocking, half serious endearment.

'And then find yourself having to live with the consequences, hmm?' He moved towards her, lifting Lucy from her unresisting arms. He held the baby's warm cheek against his own for a few seconds, then handed her back to her foster-mother before turning back to Penny to drift one finger thoughtfully down her soft cheek, lowering his voice so Margaret couldn't hear the silky emotiveness of the soft words. 'I suppose one could call this a pro forma marriage, since you're having to pay in advance for the goods, not even sure if you'll ever receive them.' He watched her face pale, heard the hiss of her indrawn breath. Darkly intent, he gazed into her beautiful eyes. 'I hope for your sake, my love, you're awarded guardianship . . . and you never find the price too high!'

Penny hoped so too as she followed him towards where the Jaguar stood awaiting them. She had approached Saul at a time when her mind had been deranged with grief and allowed herself to be manipulated into agreeing terms she had never envisaged. That morning she had awakened feeling sick and frightened at the step she was about to take. Yet, when he had arrived to escort her to the registrar's office, Saul had seemed so calm and assured, so certain that they were doing the right thing, she had regained her confidence. She had gone through the ceremony with a calm dignity, repeating the simple words in a steady voice, and she was grateful to Saul because she had been aware of his support, and that had lessened her ordeal.

They had been travelling over an hour when he drew into the forecourt of an expensive-looking restaurant and brought the car to a halt.

'I thought we'd stop for lunch now,' he told her with a pleasant smile. 'I was entertained here myself some months ago and made a note to remember it—for when the occasion was special enough.'

'It looks lovely!' Eagerly Penny alighted, glad to stretch her legs. She'd been too nervous to eat breakfast and now her appetite was raring to go. Her voice rose in excited anticipation. 'I'm sure I'm going to enjoy it!'

The menu more than came up to her expectations, and on this occasion she had no hesitation about ordering.

'Grapefruit . . . lamb provençal . . . courgettes and mushrooms, please.' She gave her order to Saul, allowing him to instruct the waiter, astonished when, after conveying his own choice, he added. 'And a bottle of Veuve Clicquot.'

'Saul,' she leaned anxiously across the table, 'I can't possibly drink half a bottle of champagne!'

'I find that difficult to believe!' His eyebrows rose sceptically, but there was a hidden laughter lurking in the depth of his grey eyes as he caught and held her hand across the table. 'But don't feel under any obligation. It's only three glasses each, but if necessary I can manage four.'

Only, she thought about two hours later, he hadn't. In fact she doubted he'd even had two! Somehow the delicious mixture of tart and sweetness and the subtle bouquet had made each glassful slide down her dry throat like nectar.

Standing up to leave, she felt marvellous—exhilarated and a little giggly, but on top of the world. Reaching the exit, she stumbled slightly, mortified but relieved when Saul's strong arm came promptly to support her round her waist.

'I'm so sorry,' she whispered, making a determined effort to walk sedately as the cool air stung her flushed cheeks. 'I did warn you, though ...' she turned reproachful blue eyes on his amused face, 'it runs in the family, I'm afraid ...'

'Alcoholism?' Saul stopped walking to peer gravely into her troubled face. 'Now that's something you *should* have confessed, my love ...'

'No!' Uncertain in her bemused state whether he was teasing or not, she spoke emphatically. 'Inability to hold alcohol. It was just the same with Tuppy.' She smiled confidingly into Saul's surprisingly tolerant face. 'She used to pass out after just a sip ...' Penny paused, touching her hot cheek with a cool hand, wishing she didn't feel so confused. 'Only then of course she was pregnant, only she didn't know . . . Oh, dear——' She stopped, afraid she was making a fool of herself, expecting some cutting remark from the dark-browed man whose wife she had just become and who was regarding her with an odd expression.

She certainly didn't expect the light warm laugh he uttered, or the swift kiss on her cheek as he whispered in her ear, 'Don't look so distressed, sweetheart! The effects of good champagne wear off quite fast. If you can't drink a little too much on your wedding day when can you?' And then the rider, as bittersweet as the wine, 'After all, it's the only one you're ever going to have!'

The remainder of the ride to the airport, checking through Customs and passport control and the enforced wait in the departure lounge, passed in a comfortable haze. Although three hours must have elapsed it seemed only minutes before Penny found herself relaxing in the comfortable first-class seat on the short-haul Paris-bound jet.

Far below her in the dusk the Channel was covered in thick cloud. Truth to tell, her first flight was proving an anti-climax, she admitted: no sense of speed or freedom from the bonds that tied mortals to earth. To be honest, she had had more exciting journeys down the M1.

Turning away from the window, she let her glance rest on Saul, sitting deeply engrossed in *The Times*. His preoccupation gave her the opportunity of assessing his set profile. It was the first time she'd had the chance to study him so closely and in such detail. She gave a small sigh. What a challenge it would be to try and capture his features on paper! The foundation course she had taken as a teenager of sixteen had covered many aspects of graphic art, and before she had specialised in engraving she had been one of the most talented students in the life class. Now her fingers itched to hold a pad and a stick of charcoal!

Women were conditioned to think of themselves as the beautiful sex. Regarding the generosity of nature as evidenced on Saul's engrossed face, she thought it a point open to argument. Decidedly a man's body was harder, his jaw heavier, his nose and chin more dominant: but with admirable even-handedness nature had compensated for this lack of softness by giving men more luxuriant hair, thick eyelashes, wider, more sensual mouths.

Of course it varied between individuals, but in Saul's case it must have been one of Mother Nature's more generous days. From the thick springy hair, as dark as a starless sky, past the captivating light eyes with their unusual dark aureoles and mask of heavy lashes, the straight elegant nose and classically beautiful mouth to his determined chin, she had been lavish with her favours.

A strange kind of warmth suffused Penny. It had been an impersonal scrutiny, yet her body had responded to the impression she had received with a puzzling reaction: her stomach muscles tightening spasmodically as a feeling of excitement made her flesh tingle. It was the kind of thrill any artist could receive on being moved by a work of art. She had experienced something similar when wandering round the National Gallery or the Tate, but it hadn't been quite like this: and never in response to any flesh and blood individual!

Unnerved, she turned her head to resume her contemplation of the clouds. It was incredible how quickly the time had passed since Saul's prosaic proposal. True to his word, he had dealt with all the arrangements with flawless efficiency—even to the extent of organising her trousseau!

Her mouth curved in silent laughter as she recalled her fury the day he'd arrived at her flat insisting on driving her up to London to hand over to his secretary with instructions that the latter should accompany her on a tour of elegant boutiques to ensure she had everything she needed for the honeymoon.

She had been mortified both by the implicit suggestion that her own taste was suspect—although whether his doubts arose from the blue crêpe or the black wool she couldn't guess—and by the implication that Saul was accustomed to clothing other women with his secretary's assistance.

Liz dispelled her fears on the latter point within minutes of leaving the office. An elegant woman in her late forties, attractive and friendly, she had put Penny at her ease immediately. After expressing her personal sorrow on Michael's account and offering Penny her condolences for her own dreadful loss, she had continued to say how thrilled she'd been when Saul announced his intention to marry.

It seemed he had given Liz the impression that he had fallen in love with her, Penny, at first sight on the day of the christening. A tongue-in-cheek admission probably promulgated to preserve his own pride, but nevertheless she had been grateful to go along with the illusion.

In answer to her careful question about the list of boutiques Saul appeared to be familiar with, Liz had shot her a quick, knowing smile.

'It's not what you may be thinking, my dear. I can

assure you you've no cause for jealousy as far as Saul is concerned, either with the past or the present. The scars from his first marriage have taken a long time to heal. Believe me, I've worked closely with him from the early days, and until you burst into his life I would have sworn he'd remain unmarried to his dying day.'

Penny acknowledged the assurance with a wan smile. Marriage to Saul on the terms they had agreed was going to be bad enough as it was ... She could take comfort from the thought that she hadn't replaced someone in his life of whom he was truly fond. Only her own sister, she thought wearily. Saul had certainly mananged to keep that association quiet ... but then, of course, he would have had to be extra discreet with Michael working in the same company!

Aware that Liz was still speaking, she made herself listen. 'We often entertain overseas visitors,' she was explaining. 'Many of their wives want to buy the best of London fashion—somewhere above chain store and below top couturier. So many of them wanted me to stay in the shop and help them choose that Saul soon accepted the idea, and I must admit I enjoy the opportunity of keeping in touch with the latest styles!'

Liz's help had been invaluable. There was no doubting the pure sensual pleasure the beautiful trousseau gave her. She had never despised lovely clothes, merely shut her mind to their existence because she lacked not only the money to indulge herself, but also the opportunity to display them in public. Circumstances had decreed that her social life was practically non-existent.

Of course, she pondered, settling back comfortably, if their mother hadn't suffered the first of the strokes which were to prove fatal just a few months before Tuppy and she had celebrated their twentieth birthdays things might have worked out differently. As it was it had been impossible to leave the older woman alone in the house for long periods. Overriding her sister's offer, it had been Penny who had elected to leave the small studio where she had been working for the previous eighteen months to work from home. It hadn't been easy: but eventually natural ability, hard work and some friendly assistance from her ex-tutor—who had arranged an exhibition of her work at the Borough library—had paid dividends, and what she liked to think of as her 'cottage industry' had grown, blossomed, and by the time her mother succumbed to her second fatal stroke a year later, had been on the point of bearing fruit. It was then she had taken the vital decision to forge ahead on her own rather than return to the studio. Surely the worst was behind her, she had argued. She had learned most of the business pitfalls she must avoid, she had a good accountant and a steadily growing order book. What could go wrong?

In asking that question she had surely tempted fate!

Tearing her mind away from the past, she deliberately sought to raise her spirits. Thoughtfully her hand caressed the soft silk chiffon pleats of the dress she was wearing. Her wedding dress. She gave a rueful smile. She had fallen in love with it at first sight. From a mid-blue shoulder yoke beneath a small white collar, the white pleats fell to just below knee length, caught at the waist by a matching blue tie belt. Below-elbow-length sleeves softly gathered from the fashionably squared shoulder line were themselves edged with blue. Fully-lined, the dress had been elegant and demure, suitable for the

simple ceremony, and with the additon of a pure wool
reefer jacket in the same soft blue, ideal for the flight to
Europe.

'It's beautiful!' Penny had cried out spontaneously,
stepping from the cublicle to pirouette in front of an
admiring Liz. 'And what's more, I can wear the same
accessories I wore at Lucy's christening!'

At the time she had wondered why the willowy blonde
sales assistant had smiled. Only later when she saw the
price and realised that the dress had cost more than the
gross weekly income of the average British manual
worker had she realised how amusing her parsimonious
attitude must have seemed.

Under Liz's guidance she had added to her wardrobe a
jade-coloured suit in pure new wool with a straight skirt
and wide revered blouson-style jacket with a low buckled
waistband and cuffed sleeves, which came complete with
its own pure silk blouse in a snazzy jade and black print.

Again the price had staggered her, but Liz had been
quietly positive. 'Saul will be hurt if you try to economise.
He wants you to have the best available.'

Reluctantly she had given in, adding to her parcels a
stunning light wool turquoise dress with a cowl neckline
which skimmed her figure with loving fidelity and a
wide-necked full-skirted dress Liz had insisted on her
having for evening wear.

Bemused, she had resigned herself to receive suitable
accessories and the stunningly exquisite silk and lace
teddies and underslips Liz obviously considered necessary for the start of married life. Really, she had thought
with amused detachment, Saul's secretary seemed to be
getting a lot more pleasure out of this shopping

expedition than the designated recipient of all this luxury. But then Liz didn't know these delicious undies weren't going to be seen or appreciated by anyone else other than their wearer—unless Saul showed any interest in the domestic washing line!

'How about a pair of jeans and a sweater?' Penny had asked hopefully at one stage, recalling the bleached threadbare garments Tuppy had once objected to, only to be informed apologetically that Saul had made one definite stipulation—'no jeans'.

She had bridled at the unexpected ban, only slightly mollified when Liz had explained with a companionable grin that it didn't extend to trousers generally. In retrospect she had to admit the aqua linen slim-cut trousers she had finally selected were infinitely more flattering to her slender well-shaped bottom and long legs than the heavier coarse denim she had been used to wearing, and the aqua, beige and white sweater with its dolman sleeves, fluffy texture and high roll collar that complemented them turned the whole ensemble into something that wasn't just comfortable to wear but feminine and incredibly alluring.

Finally Liz had selected two nightdresses—one peaches and cream, the other lilac and grey: each so breathtakingly seductive that the very thought of Saul actually seeing her decked out in either had brought a fiery blush to her face. Panic had been followed by the reassuring thought that since money appeared to be no object and Saul was no more desirous of her intimate company than she of his, he had probably booked them into a suite at their hotel.

She bit her lip thoughtfully as the plane banked. There had been very little time for conversation between them

and she still had no idea why it suited Saul to take a wife
to Paris. Even her discreet questioning of Liz had
produced a totally negative result.

'Time to fasten your seat-belt.' Saul reached across to
complete the service for her. So deeply immersed in her
thoughts had she been, Penny hadn't heard the announcement of their imminent descent into Charles de
Gaulle airport. Paris! The word was magic. All her life
she had wanted to see the Mona Lisa and the fabulous
Winged Victory of Samothrace in the Louvre . . . and
then there was the Rodin Museum. . . . Her imagination
leapt to embrace the treasures that awaited her. While
Saul was going about his business she'd buy herself a
ticket on the Metro and enjoy all the pleasures the City of
Light promised her.

The transfer from the terminal to the hotel in the
centre of Paris was made with the smooth efficiency
which seemed to characterise all Saul's undertakings.
When the taxi finally arrived at their destination Penny
saw the size and splendour of the hotel and voiced a silent
prayer of thanks to Liz for ensuring that her wardrobe
matched the quality and style of Saul's own.

Nominally she was his wife. However reluctantly he
had decided to give her that status, by accepting it she
had accepted the fact that she owed him a public
deference and respect. She had little doubt it was a duty
he would insist on, and it was one she intended to pay
scrupulously, for her own sake as much as his!

She was still pondering on what duties Saul might
demand of her when the porter carrying their cases
stopped at a door on the third floor.

'The room is satisfactory, *monsieur*?'

Having opened the door and transported their luggage

over the threshold, he had returned the key to Saul and
was quietly awaiting his approbation.

'Quite satisfactory.' The deep tones of her husband
made an understatement as he tipped the man and closed
the door behind him.

The room was enormous with a deep rose-pink carpet
stretching from wall to wall. Matching velvet curtains
hung in tasselled bondage at the side of net-covered,
gracefully arched windows which opened out on to a
narrow wrought-iron-protected balcony. Penny's roving
eye passed quickly over the modern teak furniture, the
pink and gold wall lights, the elegant shelved and padded
headboard against which rested a large double bed, its
outer sugar-pink coverings turned back to reveal
champagne-coloured sheets and pillowslips with inset
lace panels and pink piping. Her gaze lingered in
breathless admiration on the startlingly beautiful repro-
duction of Poussin's famous painting 'Rape of the Sabine
Women' which covered the wall above the headboard:
they too had been unwilling brides, but later when the
opportunity for rescue had come they had elected to stay
with their captors . . .

She gave a poignant little sigh, as she tore her eyes
away, knowing her own 'capture' had been of her own
making and for quite different reasons. It must be as she
had surmised—Saul had booked them into a suite.
Moving quickly in front of him, she made for the door at
the far end of the room, certain that beyond it she would
find a small ante-room where her own single bed would
be awaiting her. Hopefully she opened the door—and
came to an incredulous halt.

She was looking at a large luxurious bathroom. Bath,

shower cabinet, loo and bidet . . . all were there, plus an enormous double-basined washbasin fitment—two pink ceramic bowls set in white gold-veined marble. Deep rose-pink towls hung on rails and fell suspended from gold-plated rings. There was everything she possibly needed—except another door leading to another room!

'Mmm, very well appointed.' Saul's voice sounded smugly behind her as his light touch on her shoulder confirmed his close proximity.

She turned in dismay to face him, watching his eyes narrow in perception of her frowning disapproval. 'Why, what's the matter, Penny? Don't you like the colour scheme?'

In this new environment he was subtly different, seeming to have shed the cool exterior she had grown accustomed to, and with it had gone the chilly arrogance she had schooled herself to live with. In her fertile mind, still no doubt influenced by her post-nuptial champagne indulgence, he seemed to have about him the air of a contestant, senses alert, poised and ready for the challenge ahead.

Of course, she comforted herself, he was probably psyched up for the business conference he'd told her about: but it was dawning on her by the minute that she had married a stranger and one a great deal more dangerous than she'd ever suspected.

'I thought there'd be another room,' she said carefully, having no recourse but to return his questioning look. 'I mean . . . there's only a double bed?' To her absolute self-disgust she felt the blood flame her face.

'You don't care for *le matrimonial*?' Any hope that the hotel had made a mistake died instantly as she saw the muscles at the side of his mouth twitching.

He was laughing at her! But she wouldn't be deterred. If she'd had any idea he had actually expected her to share a bed with him, she would have packed one of her old respectable cotton nighties. It wasn't seduction she was afraid of—Saul had already made it clear she held no charms for him in that respect—but the thought of having to crawl in beside him garbed in an Arabian Nights fantasy of satin and lace was humiliating! She wouldn't put it past him to assume she was trying to seduce him . . . and that had to be the very last thought on her mind!

'Not in the circumstances,' she told him bleakly.

'Well, in the circumstances, I'm afraid I don't intend to do anything about it.' He touched her small nose with the tip of one finger in a mildly remonstrative way before walking casually towards the object of discussion and lounging down upon its springy surface, while she watched him, her breasts rising and falling rapidly with a breathlessness that wasn't normal. 'It seems of an adequate size and comfort to accommodate both of us.'

'That's not the point!' She rejected his indifference hotly. After all, he'd deliberately led her to believe she wouldn't have to share the same room as him—let alone this!

An experienced glance travelled thoughtfully over her shapely body, its curves enticingly hinted at beneath the pristine white silk of her wedding dress, registering the tenseness that had tightened her jawline and brought her hands together in a rigid clasp.

'The *point* is, Penny, as you already know, I have important business here in Paris, and the *fact* is that this room was booked several months ago when I believed my companion was going to be a lady who would consider anything but a double bed an insult to her seductive charms,' Saul replied with an amused composure, watching calmly as she gave a small gasp of shock.

'You were bringing some—some strange woman here!' Outrage registered in her tip-tilted chin as disdain darkened her eyes.

Saul shrugged with a nonchalant ease that dismissed her disgust with scant regard. 'Strange to you, certainly: but not to me. There's more than one lady of my acquaintance who would have accepted such an invitation with alacrity.' The smile he turned on her astounded face was devilish. 'Now, of course, you've provided me with a far better reason for coming to Paris than an illicit weekend.'

CHAPTER SIX

BEFORE the laughter in those bright, taunting eyes, Penny's glance flickered and fell. It was unforgivable of Saul to spring these shocks on her when she felt so gauche and uncertain. She sensed he was actually enjoying her indignation and she detested him for it!

'Why did you need a reason?' she asked eventually into the silence as curiosity overcame her distaste.

'To disguise the real purpose of my business. The man I've come here to see is a highly influential Arab statesman who comes to Paris every year for a medical check-up. His presence at this time will, therefore, go unremarked on. But it so happens there are moves afoot in his country to build a large sea-water desalination plant. Plans have already been submitted by an Eastern bloc country, but my acquaintance would prefer the contract to be given to a UK consultancy.'

'And he chose you?' With eyes widening in astonishment Penny awaited his reply.

'He did,' Saul confirmed her query, one dark eyebrow lifting sardonically at her overt disbelief. 'He's already familiar with other successful projects I've had a hand in and he wants to have all relevant details regarding the site including geological and land surveys that will make it unnecessary for me to make a personal visit to the Gulf. From this information he hopes I'll be able to provide a design and written specification more efficient and economical than that presently favoured by his compatriots.' His face was serious now, the skin stretched tightly across his carved cheekbones as he demanded her attention. 'It's an extremely sensitive situation. My contact is acting unofficially. The surveys are so confidential they can't even be trusted to a messenger, let alone the post. Contact has to be personal between the two principals concerned. If I can come up with something obviously superior my contact will have a good case for contesting the current plans, but if his intentions are suspected at this stage by anyone in opposition to him, either through political or personal motives, his career . . . not to mention his life . . . could be in danger.'

'Industrial espionage?' Penny's lips curled scornfully.

'No.' Saul made a laconic denial. 'A dangerous patriotism on his part . . . and for me, an irresistible challenge.' The annoying smile was back in evidence. 'So you see I had to have a very good camouflage for being here—a personal reason that in the event of my being recognised would be strong enough to justify my visit on those grounds alone.'

'You're that well known?' Penny stared at him in disbelief, her eyebrows tilted questioningly. 'Funny, I didn't see the photographers at the airport mob you!'

'There's no need for sarcasm.' The dangerous sparkle in his eyes reproved her. 'You obviously don't read the right media. In my own line I'm very well known. We're talking in millions, my sweet wife—and at that level there's plenty of international interest and the professional grapevine is very fruitful.' As if to pay her back for her attempt at irony Saul let his eys travel with slow masculine appreciation over every line of her body, before returning them to her face, their tantalising gleam deliberately provocative. 'Now, of course, I have the best possible reason for throwing industrial prowlers off the scent—a romantic honeymoon in the City of Dreams with my newly acquired wife!'

'You married me for a few paltry thousand pounds because your girlfriend let you down!' Penny's spirited challenge sprung from utter humiliation. Heaven knew their marriage was a mockery, but she had believed the cause to be charitable rather than mercenary.

Saul's cynical smile deepened. 'Millions, not thousands,' he corrected calmly. 'And no one let me down. Once I'd decided to marry you the invitation was never made.'

'Then it should have been!' she stormed angrily, oblivious to the dilation of the midnight pupils in his clear grey eyes. 'You should have had your dirty weekend first instead of making me a party to your doubtful intrigues!' For some unaccountable reason she felt like crying.

'Your proposal made that impossible.' His tone was stripped of emotion. 'Once I'd been persuaded Lucy's future lay in my hands and the solution was marriage between you and me, how could I have insulted you by coming away with another woman a few days before the wedding?'

'I wouldn't have cared,' she lied recklessly, knowing she would have felt dreadful, especially as Liz would almost certainly have known. It was also absurd for her to resent his using her for his own purposes when she had subjected him to the same treatment, and she was angry with herself for her illogicality.

'Yes, you would,' Saul corrected gently. 'You've got a stubborn pride which doesn't take easily to the curb, and in that particular instance you would have been justified in your resentment.' She was treated to a hard appraisal from smoky eyes. 'It wasn't the way I chose to begin our association.'

'It's your intention to put a curb on me?' Penny offered him a scornful smile, aware that the situation was deteriorating badly but unable to hide her vexation. She was trembling with a mixture of anger and apprehension as she faced him, her heart hammering, the pulse at her throat making her aware of its presence. She didn't want to fight this difficult stranger she'd tied herself to, but there were limits to what she would endure at his hands and he couldn't expect her total unconditional capitulation to his dictates.

'Listen to me, Penny.' The words came across deeply and smoothly as he rose to his full height to glower down at her, his eyebrows knitting in exasperation as she took an instinctive step away from him. 'We both know the score. We're committed to a purpose and our personal feelings to each other must take second place to ensure its success. But, as my wife, you will be expected to give me your total loyalty when I demand it—as I do now. I want you to give the performance of your life outside this room to convince any observers that we're so in love we have no time for anyone or anything else!' He paused, anticipating objections. When he received none he continued in a slightly milder tone. 'The reason I've been so frank with you is to let you know I could have obtained the co-operation I needed without difficulty from another source but at the expense of your pride. I believe that entitles me to your consideration, don't you?'

Penny supposed it did, and provided the farce was for public edification only she supposed she could manage it.

It wouldn't be beyond her capabilities to grit her teeth and subject her overbearing husband to a display of public adoration. She allowed herself a cool smile. 'Very well,' she accorded sweetly, 'I'll do my best to look like a besotted bride. And now, if you'll excuse me, I think I'd like to change for dinner.' Hurriedly she sidestepped past his tall figure to grab her suitcase and seek the sanctuary of the bathroom with it.

Locking the door with hands that shook, she leant back against it, trying to control her ragged nerves. She had the oddest possible feeling that she had bitten off more than she could chew, and the only solution was for her to train her appetite to cope with the idiosyncratic demands of the man on the other side of the door. At least, she consoled herself with a forced optimism, nothing would ever be as bad as this again. Once they were back in England there would be no need for pretence. It would only be a couple of days.

She took her time emerging showered, made-up and delicately perfumed, clad in the elegant turquoise wool dress which moulded her figure to perfection.

'Will I do?' she asked defensively, surprised at her own nervousness as Saul abandoned the paper he had been reading to scan her from head to foot with a con-noisseur's attention to detail. A small panicky sensation rose inside her, then he smiled with unexpected charm.

'If you can play the part as beautifully as you look it, your success is assured, sweetheart.'

He was on his feet with unexpected speed, his arms holding her and turning her towards the window where concealed lights cast their pink glow on her unblemished skin. One hand steadied her chin as if expecting her to draw away as he lowered his head to touch her mouth with his own in a fleeting salutation. The warm brushing of his lips was like a brand, taking her breath away. For one heady moment she sensed a surge of response within herself—an unlikely reaction which died the moment she saw the cynical glitter in his fine eyes which told her the caress had only been a cue to make her entry on to the waiting stage a little easier.

Seated in the softly lit restaurant of the hotel enjoying a delicious helping of roast duck with black cherry sauce after having titillated her palate with mouthwatering smoked salmon rolled and stuffed with prawns in cream sauce, Penny was prepared to admit that Saul was playing his own part with all the considerate charm of a devoted lover.

Clearly when he wanted something he went for it full tilt—no holds barred! It was a characteristic they shared and not one likely to presage a peaceful co-existence if their interests clashed. Tonight they didn't.

Her nerves soothed by the light fragrant white wine, her appetite satisfied by the good food stylishly served, her trembling anxiety calmed by the background music, Penny found herself relaxing and beginning to enjoy Saul's company.

There was something very flattering in his close attention, the dark head inclined to catch her every word, his astonishing eyes warm with pretended affection fixed to her animated face. False as she knew it to be, she felt herself bloom beneath the caress of those lustrous eyes, her personality expanding beneath the warmth of his smile like a rose opened beneath the kiss of the sun, she thought fancifully, laughing at her own imagery, yet tremulously aware that never in her life had she felt more attractive.

'Tell me,' said Saul conversationally as she politely declined having her glass refilled—the lunchtime's lesson well remembered—'your sister surely wasn't christened Tuppy, was she?'

'Heavens, no!' Penny's lips curved in a soft smile of remembrance. 'Her real name was Philippa, but as a child I couldn't pronounce it properly so it became "Fluppa". Then one day an elderly neighbour seeing us playing together referred to us as "Penny Plain" and "Tuppence Coloured" . . . after that the name stuck.'

'Not only elderly but in his dotage,' Saul said drily, then in reply to her questioning look, 'My dear Penny, no one could possibly call you plain!'

It was a nice compliment, well befitting a bridegroom, and Penny acknowledged it with a bright smile of appreciation.

'Well, certainly comparatively plain,' she insisted primly. 'Tuppy was a raving beauty even at six. All the boys were crazy about her—but she was never vain or selfish. Do you know, we were so close we used to share everything—clothes, books, make-up . . . even our diaries. Every weekend we used to swop over and read what the other one had written!'

She couldn't help the small sigh that escaped her parted lips. They had been such happy, fun-loving days, ending when they had both left school to go their separate ways.

Staring down at her plate, the reference to diaries having forcibly reminded her of what she had read so recently in Tuppy's beautiful neat hand, Penny swallowed the sudden lump that had risen in her throat. The brief but passionate liaison with Saul was one thing Tuppy had never mentioned to her. What an irony it was that she was still in a sense sharing with her sister. 'Saul begged me to reconsider marriage,' Tuppy had written; and now, across the table from her, regarding her with unfeigned interest, was the same man her twin had loved and rejected.

'Tell me more about your background. What happened to your parents?' Saul's softly voiced question made her lift her eyes, glad to change the pattern of her thoughts; although the answer still dwelt on tragedy, at least it wasn't so recent . . . or so raw.

'My father died when we were six,' she told him prosaically. 'Some accident at the chemical plant where he worked as a draughtsman. Mother was wonderful, she worked very hard to see we never went without anything we really needed.' Saul's slight nod encouraged her to continue. She suspected that he already knew something of her past where it touched Tuppy's. Still, if he wanted more information about her she was quite happy to provide it.

'Tuppy and I both left school at sixteen,' she continued after a moment's hesitation to collect and arrange her thoughts. 'I went to college on an arts foundation course and Tuppy toyed with the idea of modelling, but decided instead to join a local public relations company. They were very keen and go-ahead, and within two years they'd moved to London and taken her with them as their star demonstrator-cum-hostess.' A note of pride entered her voice. 'She made all the best shows and technical exhibitions.'

'Yes, I know.' Saul seemed temporarily lost in his own thoughts. 'I met her at one shortly after Michael had told me he wanted to marry her. Purely by chance . . .'

A small sharp pain constricted Penny's chest, and blindly her hand rose to meet it. Dear Heaven . . . from such small beginnings . . .

Impatience and self-annoyance wiped away an answering pain she had glimpsed on Saul's face. As if embarrassed at betraying himself, he frowned, saying brusquely, 'So Tuppy was out earning her living while you weren't contributing anything to the family budget.'

'Yes, that's right.'

She refused to let him see how much the inference behind the question hurt her. She wouldn't defend herself before this self-composed man whose softly voiced gibes flayed her sensitivity. Besides, what he said was true. Tuppy had been earning, enjoying every minute of a life filled with innovation and excitement and meeting new people on a daily basis, while she herself had been at college, ever fearful she might not be able to justify the confidence invested in her ability.

'Go on . . . I'm interested.' Across the table Saul's curious eyes invited her confidence. 'What happened next?'

Briefly she paraphrased her career. 'I left college determined to make a career out of glass engraving and following a recommendation was taken on by a studio in a junior capacity. I worked there for nearly two years before Mother became ill. She couldn't be left, you see. She was semi-paralysed from a stroke.' She swallowed hard, suddenly unable to control a surge of emotion. It wasn't as if Sarah Kingston had been *old*, barely fifty, and she hadn't even lived long enough to know her grandchild!

A warm hand found hers across the pristine tablecloth.

Saul's fingers interlaced with her own, surprisingly strong and comforting.

'So you stayed at home to look after her,' he prompted softly.

She nodded. 'Tuppy was a great help. She made regular visits, and even appointed herself as my London marketing agent! I owe her so much. She brought in a great many clients from amongst her friends and associates—many of them still with me.'

'Yet after your mother died and Tuppy wanted you to go and live near her, you refused?'

So her living arrangements had been discussed with Saul and he'd remembered the conversation. Ought she to feel gratified? From the mocking look on his face she thought not.

She made a small gesture with her hand, drawing it away from his clasp. 'There were many reasons why it would have been a mistake . . .'

'Especially as you'd begun to spread your wings and enjoy a hectic social life. Tell me, Penny . . . how long was it before you made yourself into the star of your own little arty circle?'

'Hectic social life . . .?' Astonished, Penny's voice tailed into nothing. Cooped up in a small flat, desperately trying to make ends meet and pay the rent? If it hadn't been for the small legacy from her mother she would have had no option but to return to the studio and throw away everything she had so painstakingly built up. But hectic social life? Saul had to be joking!

'There's no point in denying it.' A flicker of impatience crossed Saul's brow. 'Whenever I saw Michael and Tuppy socially they were always apologising for your absence caused because you had some previous engagement . . . some heavy date you couldn't break.' He stopped speaking to raise a quizzical eyebrow at her. 'I began to believe I was destined never to meet you!'

A surge of mutiny stiffened Penny's spine as she read the mocking awareness in his steady gaze and knew without the shadow of a doubt he was remembering the first time they had in fact met!

For a moment she was tempted to tell him the truth. How she had invented a circle of friends and activities to lull her sister's fears that she was lonely and unloved. Although Tuppy and Michael hadn't been married at the time of Sarah Kingston's death they had been living together, and she had had no wish to intrude on their closeness.

After their marriage her resolve to live a distance away had hardened. Michael was a darling, devoted to his wife, but she had a sneaking idea that because of the unique closeness between herself and her twin sister, he might come to resent her continual and immediate presence in their lives. There was no accounting for the forms a possessive man's jealousy could take!

Of course there had been practical reasons too for not moving, and in truth, she had been quite content to stay in the suburbs. The previous May, after two weeks spent caring for Lucy while Tuppy was in hospital, she had been only too pleased to regain the sanctuary of her peaceful little apartment. She might be alone, but she wasn't lonely: there was a subtle but important difference between the two states which her gregarious sister had been unable to appreciate!

Besides, she thought crossly, it was absurd to say she always turned down invitations. Saul seemed conveniently to have forgotten the many times he himself was out of the country! Although to be honest she *had* refused invitations when she'd known Saul was to be present. She had had a nasty suspicion Tuppy had been engaged in match-making, and she had been determined not to be presented to Michael's eminent employer as 'available'!

That was an even greater irony in the present circumstances! It was impossible to prevent the warm blush stealing over her face.

'There's no need to look so distressed.' Saul's godlike mouth curled in derision as he watched her discomfort. 'I don't have many illusions about you, my pretty Penny, and I can assure you that neither of them criticised the fact that you were enjoying yourself in your own way. Their only concern was about your future happiness.'

'Very possibly,' Penny agreed tersely, seeing from his expression that Saul was determined to put his own interpretation on events and realising it would be futile to attempt an explanation.

Tuppy had certainly been concerned, wanting her sister to enjoy a rewarding personal relationship. Firmly believing Penny's lack of fashion-consciousness prevented her from making the visual impact she was capable of, she had taken the first steps to overcome her twin's natural reserve by giving her the fabulous dress and exotic underwear designed to make the butterfly emerge from the chrysalis.

Recalling the way Saul's eyes had dwelt for a few searing seconds on the thrust of her pale breast beneath the stretch of crêpe when she arrived at the church with Lucy in her arms, she felt the hot blood intensify in her cheeks. The butterfly had emerged with a vengeance!

'At least you've still got the grace to blush!'

The ironic observation froze her tongue. Sarcastic devil, she condemned him mutely: for ever goading her as if he expected some humilating admission from her!

She lifted a graceful shoulder, forcing herself to smile. 'At times family concern can be embarrassing, you know . . .'

'No, I'm afraid I don't.' Abruptly Saul's face lost its touch of ironic humour as his jaw tightened and a harsh note entered his deep voice. 'You see, I didn't have the benefit of a family life after my mother's death.' A contemptuous dismissive flick of his fingers. 'Oh, I do have a father somewhere, but I haven't seen or spoken to him since I was sixteen and left school.'

The casual dismissal of his parents shocked Penny into instant response. 'But that's dreadful!'

His matter-of-fact statement hadn't asked for sympathy, but she found herself unable to suppress it. Her own father was only a vague memory, but he remained a precious part of her childhood experience.

Glad to have the spotlight taken off her own background and to be given the oppportunity of finding out more about the stranger she had married, Penny leaned forward slightly, her eyes alive with a warm compassion.

'Did he remarry, then?' she asked spontaneously, wondering what kind of woman would reject her stepson. Or perhaps Saul had been the one to do the rejecting.

Looking at the sudden bitterness that ravaged his face, it wouldn't surprise her.

'Not that I'm aware of.' He took a long draught of wine. 'In fact it's most unlikely. He was devoted to my mother.' There was a pause while Saul appeared to be considering the advisability of amplifying his statement.

Penny waited quietly, sensing the turmoil of his memories. When he spoke again the flat empty tones of his voice warned her how painful the topic was to him.

'Unfortunately he held me responsible for her death.'

'Oh, no!' Remembering her own heated accusation about his involvement with making Lucy an orphan, Penny shot him a look of dismay, prepared to change the subject. Something in his half-shuttered eyes made her hold her tongue as his mouth twisted in a wry grimace.

'She was killed trying to save me from the wheels of a container lorry after I'd run out into the road. I was just seven years old when it happened.'

Pain arrowed through Penny as she visualised so clearly the guilt and grief of the young boy, their traces still left on the face of the adult man. Unwilling tears sprang to her eyes.

'Hey, if I'd known it would upset you that much I wouldn't have told you!' Saul cast her an oddly assessing look as if surprised she could find tears on his behalf.

'I'm sorry.' Embarrassed, Penny stared down at the tablecloth. 'I guess I'm sentimental.'

A mocking irony sounded in his soft answer.

'That tender heart of yours is going to get you into all kinds of trouble one day.'

So what would be new? It had already landed her in her present quandary.

Penny forced a tremulous smile to her lips, afraid of incurring his displeasure. New brides weren't supposed to sob over their dinner!

Saul lifted a dismissive shoulder. 'It all happened a long time ago. Immediately after the funeral my father sent me away to an exclusive boarding school. When I came home for the holidays he made a point of being absent, leaving me in the hands of a series of housekeepers, most of whom didn't give a damn . . .'

'Oh, Saul!' Penny sighed in commiseration. No wonder he was so determined Lucy would always have an adult male figure in her life!

Compelling eyes dwelt searchingly on her expressive face before Saul shrugged away the compassion he read there.

'It took me all of the next seven years to come to terms with the fact that he wasn't ever going to forgive me. Up till then I'd been working hard to impress him. After that . . . well, I worked even harder, but for a different reason.' A deep anger curdled the timbre of his voice. 'I wanted to beat him at his own game. He might not care for me—but, by God, he'd live to respect me!'

CHAPTER SEVEN

THERE was distant look on Saul's shuttered face as he looked down into the brandy glass, swirling the contents gently in his cupped palm. Penny found her attention held with total effect, her mind blocking out all other sound in the crowded restaurant as her gaze stayed anchored to the hard, chiselled bones of his face—drawn to his contained pain like steel to a magnet. Instinctively she knew he had never spoken to anyone else of the primitive desires that had made him what he was. Hardly daring to breathe lest she broke the growing empathy that seemed to be drawing them together, she encouraged him to continue with a gentle nod of her head.

'There's very little more to tell.' He lifted one shoulder in a negligent shrug. 'My father was a consultant engineer and I determined to follow in his tracks and then overtake him. Fortunately I received every encouragement in school and tremendous support from my tutor when I took my degree in engineering and physics. After that it was a matter of getting two years' professional training followed by a further two years in the field before I could achieve what I'd set out for—becoming a chartered engineer at the minimum possible age.'

Having tasted the triumph of personal success herself, although on a much more limited scale, Penny guessed the joy his achievement must have given him.

'Did your father ever know how well you'd done?'

'Not from me.' His smile was thin-lipped. 'By then

whatever I could achieve was for my own satisfaction only.' He paused as Penny watched the shadows of unhappy memories dull the brilliance of his eyes. 'I was twenty-five and finding the attainment of professional honours the most powerful orgasm of all. I had time for little else.'

He'd given her an opening she couldn't pass. Thirteen years lay between them, and a lifetime of experience as far as Saul was concerned. Surely he would understand her curiosity—even if he wasn't prepared to indulge it.

'Yet you found time to marry?' she hazarded daringly.

She needn't have worried. There was no sign of annoyance as he nodded. 'To get married, yes. To stay married, no.' He savoured his brandy thoughtfully, running his tongue appreciatively round firm lips as he continued to cradle the last dregs in the glass. 'Samantha was very young, very beautiful, with the face of an angel. I was older in years but a great deal younger in terms of experience . . . only of course I didn't know that until after we were married.'

Watching his solemn face, aware that Saul was deeply locked into his own traumatic past and quietly amazed that he was prepared to be so frank with her, Penny waited, wondering what was to come.

Eventually he spoke again. 'She wanted constant attention, and excitement with a capital "E"—neither of which I was able or willing to provide. In those days I was naïve enough to believe marriage meant mutual love and fidelity, innocent enough to believe in the vows we'd taken . . . and Samantha never stopped laughing at my gullibility . . .'

Grey eyes met Penny's face without flinching, inviting her to share his ex-wife's mirth. If only she could find the right words to say; gentle, comforting words to fall like a balm on the heated scars he was revealing. Penny knew she was witnessing a self-immolation of a rare intensity and finding herself unable to offer the assurances she felt he needed.

Up till then she had thought Saul's cruelty was reserved for her alone, but this deliberate exposure of his feelings was a self-inflicted torture she hadn't anticipated when she had questioned him. It was almost as if he was giving her a chance to retaliate against him, to add her voice to his ex-wife's hilarity. A strange feeling that any word she did utter would be twisted and honed into a dagger to add to his pain kept her silent, glad when he released her troubled gaze to toss the remains of the brandy down his throat.

'Fortunately for me she made a bad slip-up and became pregnant. The truth didn't dawn on her until it was too late to do anything about it. We'd both known from the start the child couldn't be mine, but when it was born it was apparent it was genetically impossible for me to have been the father. After that divorce was a formality.'

Abruptly he pushed his chair back, rising to his feet in a smooth athletic movement. A slight smile tugged at his mouth, belying the aching void of loneliness Penny was sure she had glimpsed before the lowered flare of ebony lashes had denied her the right to look through his clear eyes into his soul as he moved round to rest his hands on the back of her chair.

'And now I've unveiled my past for you, we have to think of the present. If we stay in here any longer no one's going to believe this is the first night of our honeymoon—are they?'

Obediently Penny allowed him to help her rise. How many other women had there been between the beautiful faithless Samantha and her own lovely sister? she wondered. That Saul had adored Samantha she never doubted. Her fickle defections had wounded him deeply, despite the offhand way he had dismissed the termination of his marriage. How terrible to love so completely and be deceived so utterly!

What would it be like to love and be loved by such a man? she pondered. There was a fierce courage housed in Saul's impressive body that she couldn't help but admire. At least, since she didn't love him, his power to hurt *her* would be limited. Odd, though, that already his small barbs could sting her so painfully. Penny hoped he would soon tire of baiting her. After all, she consoled herself, it had been Saul who had made the point that in Lucy's interests they had to learn to be friends!

As they moved through the restaurant she was vitally aware of Saul's fingers lightly touching her arm, guiding her between the tables with an assumed tenderness calculated to convince any interested person that he could hardly keep his hands off her.

His arm was still round her shoulders as they reached their room. In the soft glow from the wall lights the bed seemed to dominate the room. If Penny had been apprehensive about sharing it with the saturnine man at her side earlier, now, with the illusion of a false intimacy colouring her reaction to him, Penny was more disquieted than ever.

Uncertain how she was going to undress modestly, and besieged with a painful shyness, she twisted away from the weight of his arm to perch on the edge of the bed, drawing her long legs up beneath her.

As if he was aware of her instinctive withdrawal from their previous friendly familiarity, Saul cast her a look alive with cynical amusement as with what she classed as a total lack of consideration for her feelings he began to shed his clothes. Quickly she averted her gaze, infuriated by her own uneasiness, but unable to mask it.

'This is where the traditional story has a changed ending.' The provocative murmur had her glancing covertly at his amused expression, the colour rising in a betraying flush on her face. *He* might find her situation laughable, but despite the impression he had of her she was a very private person, totally unused to the casual intimacy of sharing a room with even a girl friend, let alone a strange male! And despite his recent confidences he remained just that!

A room key swung before her lowered eyes, suspended from lean capable fingers. 'In a few moments I fear I have to leave my eager bride to keep a rendezvous elsewhere.'

Relief flooded through her. 'Your meeting's tonight?' Surprise at the time of the conference arched her brows above limpid blue eyes as a merciful sense of having escaped an awkward situation brought a smile to her lips. She was going to be left alone—and in all probability would be asleep when he returned.

'What better time could there be?' Already he had divested himself of his shirt, tie and jacket. Now with a casual indifference to her fascinated regard he stepped out of his trousers, sending them to join the rest of his clothes on a chair before turning to the wardrobe to select a pair of dark cords from its depths. It was clear the meeting was to be not only private but informal too. 'No one's going to suspect a bridegroom of spending his wedding night locked into a business consultation, is he?' He didn't wait for her agreement. 'The man I'm meeting is already staying here and the key in my possession will admit me directly to his suite.'

'That's very neat,' Penny murmured her approval,
beginning to relax as she anticipated the pleasure of
being left alone to her own devices. She would be able to
study her plan of the Metro system and the layout of Paris
as well as brushing up on her French vocabulary.
Unwittingly she found her gaze following the line of
Saul's body as, back turned to her, he continued to survey
the inside of the wardrobe. It wasn't the first time he had
stripped off in front of her, but it was the first time she
had dared to look at him: really look. God, but he was
beautiful! The realisation burst on her with awesome
clarity as her curiosity was rewarded. He hadn't needed
expensive suits to compensate for any physical de-
ficiency, she determined. There was none. From the
broad balanced shoulders to his leanly muscled waist and
beyond, past his hollowed flanks covered in a dark brief
underslip to his long powerful legs, Saul van Diemen was
a breathtaking specimen of virile masculinity at its peak.
And she should know. Many a time she had sketched the
male form in life classes, enough to know that men with
the attributes displayed so unselfconsciously before her
didn't pose for a few pounds an hour in art colleges. Not
when there was a fortune waiting for them in the
advertising industry . . .

Enjoying the esoteric pleasure the sight of near-
perfection always gave her, Penny found herself mentally
sketching the power-packed frame in front of her,
identifying as she had been taught the shape and
development of male musculature, her practised eye
moving leisurely from the smooth deltoids of his upper
arm to the equally smooth interleaving soleus grouping
that shaped and strengthened his calves.

It was only when she realised the object of her study
was remaining unnaturally still that her forehead

wrinkled with sudden concern. Fearful her close scrutiny
had been observed and resented, she slowly raised her
glance upward—to have her worst fears confirmed.

A steady grey-eyed stare clashed with her apologetic
smile. 'Is there something wrong, Penny?'

She experienced an odd prickling of nerves at his soft
intonation. 'No, of course not!' she hurriedly assured
him, swallowing down her confusion. 'As a matter of fact
I—I was just wondering if you did weight-training.'

It was as near the truth as she dared get. She wasn't at
all sure her newly-taken husband would understand the
difference between artistic and sexual appreciation, and
she had no wish to make a fool of herself. Besides, it was
a fair question. His body was too smoothly yet powerfully
developed to be the result of a sedentary career.

'Some.' He answered her supposition laconically. 'I
happen to believe it's a mistake for a man to exercise his
brain at the expense of his body. To my way of thinking
the two are inseparably linked in the all-rounded *homo
sapiens*. Actually I much prefer to play squash or tennis,
but it isn't always easy to get a partner at short notice.'
He gave her a crooked smile devoid of malice.
'Sometimes when the need for physical action becomes
imperative I find lifting a few weights is the best way to
dispel tension and unwind.'

'*Mens sana in corpore sano*!' Penny nodded her russet
head eagerly, not to be outdone in the Latin quote stakes,
and happily relieved she had got the conversation on to a
non-controversial sporting basis. 'Yes, I know how you
feel. When things got beyond me at college I used to put
on a track suit and run . . .'

She stopped suddenly, vaguely aware that it was a long
time since she had felt so physically uncomfortable. Her
hands plucked nervously at the luxurious bedcover. Why

on earth didn't Saul get his casual clothes on and stop staring at her like that? Heaven knew, if she'd thought to bring a jogging suit with her, nothing would have pleased her more than to be heading at a fast trot towards the Bois de Boulogne at that very moment!

'What's the matter, then, my pretty Penny, hmm?'

Far from putting more clothes on, Saul abandoned the cords he had been holding to approach even closer, an odd glitter in his narrowed eyes that unnerved her still further.

She found her whole body shrinking away from what she was forced to recognise as a potently threatening male presence. Even the deep husky tones of his voice disturbed her. Desperately she fought down the hollow feeling in her stomach that experience warned her preceded panic.

'It's just that I'm a bit awkward, I guess,' she confessed unhappily. 'I hadn't realised we'd be sharing a room and—well, for pity's sake, although we're married I don't really know you at all. You're little more than a stranger!' Her proudly raised chin defied him to laugh at her reluctance.

'You mean you don't know what a man looks like?'

The sheer disbelief in the question would have been insulting if he hadn't been aware of her background in the arts.

'No, of course I don't mean that!' she snapped, casting him a reproachful look as the sight of his naked chest brought back the mortifying scene she ached to forget.

The soft laugh he gave made her toes curl. 'I'm sorry you seem to find the sight of my body so unnerving. If our courtship had lasted a little longer, I can assure you it would hold few surprises for you on your wedding night.'

Penny shifted uneasily, disturbed by the increased

rhythm of her heart. The conversation was taking an unexpectedly personal turn she hadn't anticipated and certainly didn't welcome. The fact it had been her own stupid fault for staring so hard at Saul's unclothed body in the first place was no consolation.

She had unwittingly invited his teasing, she admitted, and intuition told her this was only the start of it. The plain truth was, she wasn't used to being the subject of sexual banter. Working alone, her contact with contemporaries had been severely limited. It wasn't that she was prudish either. She could laugh as well as the next girl at sexual innuendos and double meanings when she read them or saw them on TV, but she wasn't used to being the butt of such humour and it made her feel uncomfortable, especially in the outlandish situation she had devised for herself.

To her growing horror Saul covered the last few steps that separated them, to sit beside her on her bed, taking her firmly by the shoulders and forcing her to face him.

'And if you find the sight of what you've seen disturbing, my beauty, have you any idea of how I feel not having seen one inch of your fabulous naked body— apart from your face and hands—since the day we first met and you dazzled my eyes with your glorious breasts and silky thighs?'

A long inward shudder racked Penny's imprisoned body. This was a thousand times worse than she'd expected! The soft drawling voice, the intent narrowed stare of his dark-pupilled eyes, the burning heat of his hands as they moved lightly on her wool-covered arms, told her he wasn't teasing just for the fun of it. It had to be the wine and brandy talking! Those and perhaps the lingering memory of the pretence they'd enacted. But theirs was a loveless union and she wasn't going to let him forget it. He had demanded her co-operation in public—but that was as far as she was prepared to go.

Penny looked at his dark face, frighteningly aware of the heavy thudding of her heart, the heavy coil of heat that seemed to be building up inside her, and read the purpose in every intent bone of his body.

'No, Saul!' she cried hoarsely, trying to tug herself free.

'Oh, yes, my pretty Penny . . .'

Swift as her recoil was, Saul's reaction was quicker. Before she could move he had used the weight of his body to force her backwards, cushioning her head in the downy pillow while his mouth sought the smooth length of her throat. She tensed unbearably as the sweet warmth of his mouth scorched a fiery trail on her soft skin.

'Saul . . .' It was a moaning prayer for mercy, but her dazed eyes, seeking release, met only the darkened pupils of his, seemingly devoid of intelligence, powered by animal instinct, and Penny knew with an aching desperation that her voice hadn't penetrated through the aura of sexual excitement that held him entrapped.

'Saul . . .!' she implored, louder this time, only to find his name stilled on her tongue as he raised his head to find and capture her mouth, kissing her deeply with a tantalising urgent hunger. Head swimming, mind incapable of coherent thought, her body moved independently to her will. Somewhere in the deep recesses of her mind she knew she was meeting his lips with a fervour of her own, hunting in his sweet hot mouth as if she could punish him for his daring by capturing his intrusive tongue and devouring it! Even before she heard the deep growl of pleasure that purred in the golden throat of the man whose aroused body subdued her she realised she was punishing no one but herself.

Damn him! She daren't scream. Not only would it be

too humiliatingly embarrassing for her, but it wouldn't help his business plans to advertise her repulsion of him. Perhaps if she just lay still, unresponsive, he would come to his senses . . .

It was then she felt his hand, dangerously erotic, move in a delicate caress up her calf, skimming the smooth nylon of her stockings. A sob caught in her throat. Saul had promised her a separate bedroom. Already he had broken the letter of that undertaking. She was absolutely determined he would keep to the spirit of it!

Any resolve to lie dormant exploded like a firecracker in a bonfire the moment she realised Saul's exploring hand was about to discover the secret of the fastening on the simple undergarment she wore. Determined to thwart him, she pressed her body hard against his marauding strength, blocking the passage of his fingers.

As a manoeuvre it was only partly successful. Instantly she felt the urgent power of his desire for her, and as his hand continued to travel slowly up her body to release her breasts from their flimsy covering and to tease their hardening apices, she closed her eyes, praying for inspiration.

'Saul!' The answer flashed into her consciousness as with a new urgency she beat her clenched fists on his shoulder. 'Saul, listen to me. Your meeting! What about your vital meeting?'

For several moments she thought she had failed, before he raised his head, looking down into her pleading, frightened face with passion-clouded eyes.

'You're right.' He was breathing heavily as she was released, gasping, from his confining weight. Hunching herself upright, encircling her bent knees with her arms, trying vainly to control the trembling of her limbs, Penny tugged her dress down to cover every visible part of her warm pulsating flesh.

Regaining his feet, seemingly now in full control of himself, Saul smiled down at her, an odd, twisted grimace. 'To be five minutes late would be a grave discourtesy. To delay the meeting so that I could make love to you with the time and dedication you deserve would destroy any chance of a successful outcome.' He made her a courteous, mocking little bow. 'Thank you for reminding me once again where my duty lies.'

Hardly aware of the shower running or Saul's speedy assumption of cords and leisure shirt, Penny sat motionless, immersed in her own misery. There was an ache in her throat and a stinging behind her eyelids. Close to tears, she had to come to terms with the fact that the heat of Saul's hand on her body had been enough to inflame her into a shameless abandon, to incite a hot tide of desire that was as foreign to her as it had been unsettling. Far worse was the humiliating discovery that, mixed with the feeling of relief at her deliverance, she felt a devastating, painful sense of loss!

It was several minutes after his departure before she could bring herself to undress and put on one of her exotic nightdresses before clambering into the bed.

She only hoped his meeting would go on for a long time into the night, and when he did return his mind would be full of other things and the momentary aberration of this evening forgotten.

Expecting to toss and turn, a victim of her muddled, churning thoughts, Penny was only aware of how quickly she had succumbed to sleep when she awakened the following morning to find the sunlight streaming through the window and the bed beside her empty.

For a moment she thought Saul had never returned,

then she heard the soft buzz of his electric razor from the adjoining room and realised he was already awake and getting ready to face the day. She emitted a muffled groan, hoping she would be able to cope with whatever mood she'd find him in. At least he hadn't attempted to molest her again : that was something she had to be very grateful for!

She didn't have long to wait. Seconds later he sauntered back into the bedroom, fully dressed in light slacks and a dark sweater. The smile he tossed in her direction was pleasant and impersonal, mercifully lacking any sign of the unwelcome intimacy he had made her endure the previous night.

A welcome sigh of utter relief escaped her as she struggled to sit up in bed, still half asleep but wary enough to drag the sheet upwards with her to mask the low-cut neckline of the nightdress which barely covered her nipples. 'How did the meeting go?' she asked brightly.

'Fine!'

Saul looked very fit and relaxed, his skin taut and smooth, his dark hair still damp, the faint delicious aroma of a subtle cologne adding to his very positive presence beside her.

'Of course I'll have to study the plans in very great detail—but all the necessary groundwork has been meticulously covered. Even last night I could see possibilities of improvements.'

Sensing the latent excitement behind the cool tones, Penny felt a sharp thrill of pleasure on his behalf. Give her brainpower rather than muscles in a male companion any day! It was ironical, she conceded, that the man she had married had more than his fair share of both.

As he walked leisurely round the bed towards the

window Penny's eyes stayed fixed to his movement. She
hadn't expected an apology for his lapse the previous
evening, so she wasn't disappointed when she received
none. She was prepared to believe his amorous approach
had been brought about by a number of interacting
circumstances, some of which had been her fault. She
should have borne in mind that the male of the species
was easily aroused by the propinquity of the female and
she should have behaved with more circumspection. She
wouldn't make the same mistake again. Fortunately they
were returning to England late the following day, so she
would only have to spend one further night in this
compromising situation, she told herself, taking a grain
of comfort from her own logical reasoning as she
watched Saul pull the curtains back to allow the late
autumn sunshine full access to the room.

'You were sleeping soundly when I came back,' he told
her, turning to regard her, a slight smile lifting the corner
of his mouth. 'I was afraid I'd disturb you, but you were
lost in your dreams.'

She didn't care that the amused glint in his eye and the
twitching muscle of his cheek suggested he found the
sight of her sheet-swathed body diverting. She didn't
intend to leave herself open to any more misunderstand-
ings. Truly she had no idea when he'd returned. Strange,
she had been dreading sharing a bed with him, and in the
event she wouldn't have known she had, if it hadn't been
for the indented pillow and the neatly folded pyjama
bottoms on top of it.

A warm and unexpected wave of gratitude overcame
her for the role Saul had agreed to play in her life. Eyes
widening appealingly, she met the humorous gleam he
slanted at her.

'I—I want to thank you for what you're doing for

Lucy . . . for me,' she told him earnestly. 'I want you to know it wasn't just selfishness on my part. I really do believe it's what Tuppy and Michael would have wanted for her, and . . .'

'Go on.' Silhouetted against the morning light, Saul encouraged her faltering words. 'And what, Penny?'

'It wasn't because you were the only person I could turn to, or just because you were her godfather . . . although that was important . . .' Dared she mention what she had discovered about his love for Tuppy? No, better not, caution warned her.

'Well?' he encouraged her softly. 'And what other reason made you come to me, hmm?'

'It was that moment in the church when I came over faint and you took Lucy,' she confided truthfully. 'You held her with such tenderness—and when I was desperate I remembered that.' Her gaze dropped shyly. 'I felt certain that if you did agree to give us temporary shelter we'd be able to trust you.'

'I see.' Saul's voice was curiously expressionless, as if her perception of the softness lurking beneath his tough exterior was unwelcome. 'It's very pleasant to know I have your trust—particularly as the arrangement is no longer temporary.'

'I hope I have your trust too, Saul?'

If they were to live together in peace, their relationship had to be based on mutual trust, because without the bonds of a physical relationship to unite them, it would founder.

Saul had agreed to make her his wife knowing very little about her and most of that based on false assumptions. Suddenly it was of the utmost importance how he would reply to her.

Wide-eyed, she searched his dark face for a glimmer of

favourable reaction, totally unaware of how wistful her oval-shaped face appeared to him, her hair tousled above pansy-blue eyes, her mouth devoid of lipstick, soft and warmly beseeching his approval. 'I really do mean to do everything possible to make your domestic life run smoothly. All you have to do is to give the orders and I'll carry them out to the very best of my ability.'

'That's very reassuring.' Saul spoke at last, his terse reply giving no hint as to how he had received her generous undertaking as he added drily, 'How about starting right this minute? Today we have to parade ourselves as a loving couple hell-bent on seeing the romantic sights of Paris, so the sooner you get out of bed and dressed the sooner we can start . . . and the sooner I'll be pleased!'

CHAPTER EIGHT

PENNY needed no second instruction, scuttling out of her warm sanctuary into the bathroom with a speed intended to turn her fleeing back view into a blur of colour.

A glow of happiness made her body tingle as she lathered it beneath the warm shower. It seemed there were to be no unpleasant repercussions from the stand she had taken and that Saul was going to make a real effort to establish a base of friendship between them, as she had implied the night he had first taken her back to her flat.

Using the door of the opened wardrobe as a shield in case he should look up from the papers he had settled down to study, she dressed quickly, deciding to wear the jade skirt and blouse. Later when they left to explore the city she would put on the jacket. Making a mental note to let Liz know how delighted she was with her trousseau, she closed the door and moved into the centre of the room.

'Very lovely!' Whether Saul meant her or the outfit or both didn't matter. Penny accepted the compliment with a graceful dip of her shining russet head.

It was a few minutes later at the door to the restaurant that Saul hesitated, taking her gently to one side and staring down at her, an unfathomable expression in his remarkable eyes. 'Now, this is where you have to remember the part you're playing, my lovely. You've spent a long, long night being made love to . . . you feel languorous and fulfilled, and although you're going to try and appear soignée and sophisticated your body won't let you forget the pleasure and passion it's known. It's going to show in the way you walk, the way you look around you . . . the way you look at me.' His voice deepened to a low burr of sound as his warm breath fanned her cheek. 'Particularly the way you look at me . . . understand?'

A sharp stab of inexplicable sensation speared through that same body he had been describing as the soft positive tones reawakened something of the unwilling arousal she had experienced beneath Saul's touch only a few hours earlier.

A little shiver traversed her spine, impossible to disguise, as his eyes narrowed at her discomfort. 'I want anyone in that restaurant who's interested enough to watch you walk through the door to believe you're a newly-wed bride who's spent the entire night being made love to most satisfactorily by her new husband . . . understood?'

'I'll do my best.' Penny had to swallow to relieve the sudden dryness in her throat.

'That should be more than enough, from what I've seen of you.'

'Oh!' Before she could protest that he knew nothing about her qualifications in the erotic arts, Saul had reached out to take her hand and lead her into the dining-room, where the delicious scent of hot croissants and freshly percolated coffee tantalised her senses.

His head dipped intimately towards her ear. 'That was a beautiful nightdress you were wearing in bed last night, darling.' The whisper was warmly suggestive.

'Liz chose it.'

'Mmm.' He sounded thoughtful, his lips pursing in contemplation. 'As an erotic creation for a night of love it was ideal.' Reaching their table, he pulled her chair out

for her, bending to kiss her cheek as she seated herself.
There was a lilting amusement in his darkly appreciative
voice as his lips nuzzled against her ear. 'As a camouflage
for your beautiful feminine body it was a disaster . . . an
absolute disaster.'

This time he got the effect he was after as Penny's
whole body flushed, the warm tide of blood flowing from
the soles of her feet to the roots of her hair as she
imagined the toll his eyes had taken of her unconscious
form.

From lowered lashes she glared at his impassive
features as he addressed the waiter in excellent French.
Act or no act, he was taking a fiendish delight in
embarrassing her. By proposing marriage to Saul she had
taken the initiative out of his hands. That he had
radically changed that proposal to suit himself didn't
make any difference as far as her original impudence was
concerned. With a sinking heart she suspected he was
going to make her pay for that piece of impertinence for a
long time to come!

Just when Penny had given full rein to her doubts and
uncertainties about the future, Saul whipped the ground
away from under her feet by giving her one of the most
exhilarating days of her life.

Nothing was too difficult to provide for her pleasure.
If he had really been head over heels in love with her he
couldn't have been more accommodating to her wishes,
and if he was bored by her unstinted delight in
everything she saw, he gave no sign of it.

Sitting in the back of a hired chauffeur-driven car,
Saul's arm draped lovingly round her shoulders, Penny
was treated to a grand tour of the city. On several
occasions the car was stopped and picked up later at

another destination so she could stroll where she liked, gazing into shop windows, mingling with the throng of people on the *grands boulevards* and the winding side streets with their *boucheries* and *pâtisseries* and pancake kiosks on what seemed to be every corner.

Staring with rapt appreciation into the show windows of the world-famed couturiers in the Rue du Faubourg St Honoré, she found herself laughingly refusing Saul's offer to add to her wardrobe.

'Good grief, Saul, I've got more clothes now than I've ever had in my life! Besides,' she gave him a mischievous smile, 'don't you know—London's supposed to be the fashion capital of the world now!'

But she *was* impressed, not only with the fashions and the exquisite jewellery displayed in the shops of the Place Vendôme but with the city itself—its sweeping avenues and wide open spaces, its graceful cathedrals and elegant buildings with their tiered, wrought iron balconies reaching towards the clear sky, softened by the lacy outlines of hundreds of trees, still beautiful despite their leafless nudity.

In the early afternoon Saul took her for a walk along the cobbled pathways beside the Seine before calling in at a small bistro in the Latin Quarter for a snack of delicious French bread and cheese washed down by red wine. By the time they had disembarked from an hour-long voyage down Paris's narrow pretty river with its tethered houseboats and attractive bridges in one of the famous glass-covered *bateaux mouches* all Penny's reservations were forgotten. What did it matter if Saul's indulgence was part of the pattern he had arranged? The day was developing a magic all its own.

At Penny's insistence they left the car in the Place Clichy to walk up the steep hill towards the Sacré Coeur.

Standing breathless on the top of the white steps, looking down at the spread of Paris beneath her with the stark outline of the Eiffel Tower a skeleton on the far skyline, Penny turned her laughing eyes towards Saul, slipping a hand through his arm in easy camaraderie.

'For a man more than a decade older than me, you're in very fine shape, Mr van Diemen!' she joked. 'All those steps and you're not even breathing hard!'

'Oh, don't let that decade worry you, Mrs van Diemen . . .' He moved slightly, pulling her into a more comfortable position against his hard muscular body as if to emphasise the accuracy of his claim. 'I can assure you there's no possible doubt about my stamina. '

For a brief second his luminous eyes searched her face, then before she realised his intention he dipped his head and kissed her hard and fully on the mouth, a lingering caress in which she sensed a note of savagery.

'Saul!' she protested half-heartedly, more surprised than shocked. She hadn't expected he would make such a public demonstration even to reinforce the legitimacy of their relationship to an interested party. Not that there were many of those around. Everyone seemed to be going about his or her own business.

One dark brow lifted as he laughed, showing startlingly white teeth against the remains of a summer tan. 'Why the astonishment? Have you forgotten we're on our honeymoon?'

'Hardly!' Penny turned her head, dark lashes fluttering down to hide her confusion as Saul took one unresisting hand in his own. She fancied he was having a little fun at her expense, that her reluctance to share a physical intimacy with him amused and irritated him in equal measure. A shiver trembled down her spine as she glanced away from him. There had been a challenging look in those translucent grey eyes that had her heart rate increasing alarmingly.

In an effort to dispel the sudden gloom the realisation of her own vulnerability had conjured up, she made a determined effort to change the subject, asking if he had made any further plans for the rapidly closing day.

'Certainly—if your stamina can match mine!' He grinned down at her with deliberate provocation. 'I thought we'd go back to the hotel, freshen up and go on to a small restaurant I know where we can dine and dance until the small hours.'

'Lovely!' she accorded cheerfully. The longer they were away from the cloying intimacy of that luxurious bedroom the better she would like it. If necessary she would dance all night, she determined, as an inner voice warned her that if she was fated to be held in the close embrace of the strong arms of the man beside her she would be much safer suffering his nearness in public rather than in private.

The restaurant was intimate, darkly lit and the food, as she had anticipated, excellent.

'Would you like to dance?'

They had finished their meal. Only the coffee cups and brandy glasses remained on their table to testify to that fact, reflecting the candlelight.

'Please!' Penny agreed happily, smiling up into Saul's solemn face as he offered her his arms. She felt warm and replete, her appetite ravenous after the day's events and the light lunch she had had, having been fully indulged. Having lost several pounds in weight through grief and illness she had known she could eat without worrying about putting on surplus weight. In fact, she thought, repressing the desire to giggle, she would probably feel quite relaxed and elegant now in her infamous 'god-mothers' dress!

The music from the five-piece band was soft and slow as Saul gathered her closely against his graceful athletic body. Her soft body pressed into his hard yet accommo-dating form, Penny found the two of them moved with a dual rapport, sharing a natural rhythm that moulded them into one lissom unit.

As Saul's hands tightened round her shoulders Penny automatically lifted her hands to clasp them at the back of his neck, responding to the throbbing passion of the music, the boldly printed dress Liz had persuaded her to buy for just such an occasion moving lazily against her legs.

A strange lethargy was overtaking her as she aban-doned herself to the support of Saul's strong frame, her thighs pressed to his, following their lead, her fingers moving of their own volition to touch the nape of his neck, exploring the crisp dark hair that teased their sensitive tips.

He didn't speak; just lowered his head to rest his warm cheek against her own. The pressure pleased her, his close aura delighting her with its subtle hints of cologne and brandy and a scent she couldn't identify but which somehow stirred chords of longing inside her as evocative as the sweet soaring sound of the clarinet that pierced the smoky atmosphere with its plaintive voice.

She would never know how long they danced, staying locked together as one melody ended and another took its place. She only knew that on the dance floor they had found an incredible compatibility, and while this unexpected magic lasted it acted as a soft balm to the raw pain that scarred her spirit and was the legacy of Tuppy's terrible death. By its very nature it would be a fleeting

pleasure but one which she meant to enjoy to the fullest
extent of its heady delight.

When the group took a break she allowed herself to be
led reluctantly back to their table, her steps a little
unsteady as, deprived of Saul's physical support, she
struggled to regain her own separate identity. Good grief,
what was the matter with her? She hadn't drunk all that
much, and anyway, wasn't dancing supposed to be a
good way of staying sober . . . of working off the effect of
alcohol? Not that she'd expended much energy then . . .
strange, she felt so tense yet at the same time so alive and
expectant . . . A shiver trembled through her as goose-
pimples sprinkled her upper arms.

Instinctively as she stumbled into her seat she held out
her hands towards the flickering candle in the wine bottle
that illumined the table. If only Saul would speak! But
across the table his face was enigmatic, exceedingly
beautiful in the shadowed light, but remote. Regret? Ah,
no, her heart wept. In those past moments she had felt
closer to him than ever before—no, more than that. She
had felt closer to him than to anyone else she had known.
And the feeling had been good.

Now he was repulsing her, returning to being the
stranger she had coerced into marrying her. Her teeth
fastened little-girl-like on her soft underlip as she fought
to control her spiralling emotions. If only she could think
of something to say—anything to break the quivering
expectancy that seemed to be growing in intensity by the
moment.

'For God's sake, Penny!' Saul's voice rasped across the
table at her in a husky whisper as his two hands thrust
forward to clasp and still her own where unconsciously
she had been rubbing them up and down the slender neck
of the wine bottle in rhythmic caressing movements.

'You've got every male within a radius of ten yards glassy-eyed! Do you want to start a riot?'

'What?' Astonished and totally without understanding, Penny stared down at his sensitive, competent hands. Surely a little fidgeting wasn't serious enough to make him look at her with such a pained expression?

'Come on,' he spoke roughly. 'We're leaving!'

'Oh, but Saul,' she protested her disappointment, easy tears coming to dampen her eyes, 'do we have to? Can't we stay a little longer?'

'No, we can't!' His saturnine face refused discussion. 'Now isn't the time to play the tease, if you know what's good for you!'

She gave an audible gasp as he came round the table, taking her by the shoulders and pulling her to her feet. Bewildered, she cringed from the latent savagery behind the action.

Even though the situation appeared beyond redemption she made one more plea to prolong her enjoyment. 'I don't want the evening to end yet,' she told him, her voice husky with misery, at the same time obeying him by draping her wrap round her shoulders and taking up her small bag.

'Neither do I, my darling,' he told her, an unwarranted grimness thickening his tone as the palm of his hand flat against her back guided her towards the exit. 'But the time has come when little girls should be in bed, I think.'

Too disappointed to argue, Penny bowed to the inevitable, following him out into the cool night air, her tender mouth compressed with frustration, her eyes downcast.

In the taxi Saul neither spoke nor touched her. Glancing at his taut profile, she wondered again at his sudden change of mood. It was obvious she had done something to dispel the friendly atmosphere that had surrounded them. She turned her head, feeling the beginning of a yawn stretching her throat. Perhaps it was just as well Saul had decided to bring the evening to an abrupt end, she consoled herself, feeling tiredness overtaking her. Despite his claim to enduring stamina not only had he been up half the night, but he had awakened a great deal earlier than she had. Now she was prepared to admit that her protest in the restaurant had been thoughtless.

On the way from the lift down the long corridor that led to their room she felt the wrap slip from her shoulders. Stopping to retrieve it, she watched Saul pace ahead of her with a tight-hipped aggressive stride: impatient steps that left her trailing in his wake.

What a day to remember, though! It had been like winning the top prize in a competition—a day in Paris with the man of your choice! What an irony that phraseology held! Penny smiled inwardly, wishing that Saul could have tasted even a grain of the magic that she had savoured . . .

'Oh!' A stifled scream rose in her throat. There had been a movement, a sudden overpowering presence, and she had been lifted into Saul's arms with ease and dexterity as if she had been a recalcitrant child. Too taken aback to struggle, she found herself transported at a distance-eating speed, one strong arm supporting her back, the other beneath her thighs.

Kneeing the already unlocked bedroom door open, Saul carried her through, closing it sharply with the sole of one accurately placed shoe as without pausing he continued across the room to deposit her on the bed.

Bouncing slightly in reflex action against the power with which she'd been dumped and astonished by the cavalier attitude with which she'd been treated, Penny fought to steady her breathing, watching with a growing trepidation as Saul stood over her, hands already beginning to strip off his jacket, his shirt, the belt from his dark tight trousers, the clasp at their waist . . . And all the time his eyes never left her startled face, half hidden, the irises a silvery glitter beneath the lowered fan of sooty lashes mesmerised her into unwilling stillness.

She had married a stranger. During the course of the day he had become a friend. Now he was again a dangerous unwelcome alien, with a deadly purpose priming his fine body to action and dulling his conscience. Bewildered, totally at a loss, pitifully her eyes searched the contours of his transfigured face, recognising nothing except the power of his sexual desire.

Naked now, save for the body-hugging briefs that betrayed the strength and urgency of his need, Saul lowered his hands to discard this last barrier. In that instant fear thrummed through Penny's nerves to break the stupor that had paralysed her.

Cold to the core of her being, her throat tight with panic, her limbs leaden, she scrambled towards the far side of the bed, intent only on escaping his intent to ravish her. Husband or not, this wasn't what they had agreed. She didn't want him . . . and she wouldn't have him!

Penny knew she had lost the battle the moment she felt Saul's hand grasp one nylon-clad ankle and his other hand move to pinion her shoulder as he slid it beneath the wide neckline of her dress, pushing it down one arm as his body, a firm controlling weight, trapped her where she lay.

Hot and violent, his mouth sought hers, brooking no denial to its voluptuous assault. If she had been rational she might have realised that despite the urgency of his movements Saul's caresses weren't lacking an innate delicacy. The tongue that demanded her acceptance was a flicking gentle intruder, his hand which had continued to push her dress down her body so it could capture the unprotected swell of her tender breasts nestling within the black teddy was moving with a sensual, sensitive touch, acknowledging and respecting the exquisite susceptibility of the female body.

But Penny wasn't rational. The hard pressure of Saul's thighs, the tension of his muscles as his need for her gathered impetus, had driven all logical thought from her mind.

Everything had happened too fast. She only knew that unless she could break through the heat haze of desire that had brutalised him, within the next few minutes Saul would take her unloving and unloved with a careless power as destructive as it was forceful.

Her body squirmed uselessly beneath his domination as she tried to evade him. Agonisingly she realised he was taking her spasmodic movements beneath him as encouragement.

In desperation she felt his mouth drift from her lips to emblazon her cheeks and throat with open-lipped caresses. She gave a choking frightened cry of mingled despair and pleasure as she felt her whole body respond. Nothing in her life had prepared her for the violent reactions of her own flesh beneath such a studied, ardent assault!

Lifting his head at her exclamation, Saul shifted his position slightly, propping himself up on one elbow to gaze down at her, his eyes beneath half-closed lids bright and fervid as with a deep male satisfaction he recognised the transformation he had induced.

'Beautiful,' he whispered, his voice thick and throaty. 'I thought I must have exaggerated the picture of you I carried in my mind. Now I see I didn't do you justice . . .'

She felt his shudder as if it had been her own as to her consternation he prevented her from crying out in her own vindication by lowering his coal-dark head to repossess her mouth, kissing her deeply with a slow lazy hunger that brought a ripple of heat to suffuse every inch of her sensitive skin.

When at last her mouth was freed from his fierce demanding kiss, Penny cried out in anguish, twisting her fingers in his thick hair as she tried to force his dark head away from her, knowing how inadequate the words were to express her inner turmoil.

'Stop it . . . please, please stop!'

'What is it, my darling?' Something in her frantic wail had pierced through to the dark recesses of Saul's mind, forcing him to recognise the underlying agony in her voice as having its roots in terror rather than ecstasy.

'I don't want this!' Her voice was shaking badly, broken and raw.

'What do you want, then?' There was an unusual humility in his soft voice, an eagerness to please. 'Tell me, Penny—teach me how you like to be loved.'

'I don't want to be loved at all—not by you! Not now! Not ever!'

'What are you saying?' Black-pupilled eyes, lustrous and confused, sought her distressed face, fighting for understanding.

Dear God, she prayed, has no woman ever said 'no' to him? Doesn't he understand the word?

'No!' she repeated it tempestuously. 'No, no, no! That's what I'm saying.' Her breath sawed painfully through her constricted throat.

'But why?' More puzzled than angry, Saul continued to stare at her flushed face, the tumbled deep autumn gold of her hair on the pale pillow. 'I won't hurt you. I'll wait for you . . .' Like an eager small boy begging for a favour his mouth twisted into an appealing smile. 'I won't rush you, I promise. I can wait for you—if you'll help me . . .' Before she could stop him he took her hand, intent on guiding it towards his own body.

Jerking her flesh away from his impatient hold, Penny struck out at him, catching him a glancing blow across his naked chest.

'Can't you understand English, Saul? I don't want you I just don't want you!' Harshly she repeated her rejection, reinforcing her meaning by tugging at her disarrayed clothes with trembling fingers, hiding her pale breasts and thighs from his tortured gaze.

She wasn't looking at him: daren't do so. If he chose to ignore her protests she wouldn't stand a snowflake's chance in hell of fighting him off.

Seconds of silence passed in which his laboured breathing mingled with her own dry sobs before Saul broke it.

'All right, Penny, I understand. You've changed your mind.' He gave a harsh bitter laugh. 'Only next time when you don't intend to follow through I'd advise you not to come on so hard. That kind of invitation is painful for a man to ignore—as I'm sure you know.'

'What next time?' Fury overcame her caution. 'Don't get all injured with me, Saul, because you chose to bring me with you rather than your obliging girlfriend.' Her heart missed a beat; she was amazed at her own courage. 'How dare you expect me to act as a sexual substitute for some—some immoral bitch who'd sell her body for a holiday!'

Invitation indeed! What invitation? She'd been given absolutely no choice about sharing a room. What had he expected—that she'd offer to sleep in the bath? Righteous indignation flamed through her. She was so angry she could have struck him again, only some whisper of self-preservation warned her he would only take so much and that he was perilously near that limit through no fault of her own.

'Be careful, my darling.' There was a scalding ferocity in his scornful endearment. 'Just because your price was higher it doesn't make you more virtuous—just more venal.'

'At least I don't lie and I don't cheat!' Penny squared up to him, refusing to be cowed by his insult. 'You agreed that our marriage was to be one of convenience only. You stipulated that we'd have separate bedrooms!'

If she'd punched him on the jaw he couldn't have looked more stunned. Fascinated, she watched the slow path of his larynx as it moved paroxysmally in his strong throat.

'Certainly I promised you a separate bedroom.' He shook his head as if to clear it. 'But I was talking about living space, personal privacy. I was talking about not having to spend the night with each other if we didn't want to. Hell, I was talking about being alone when we needed to be!' Saul was staring at her white, shocked face as if he had never really seen her before. 'You honestly thought I was suggesting keeping our union celibate?'

A cold sweat drenched Penny's trembling limbs. It had been exactly what she had thought. Miserably she nodded. Surely she had made it very clear to him that day she had proposed to him that she wasn't considering an intimate relationship? With a sinking heart she saw from the blank expression on his face that she had totally misunderstood his revised offer.

'You actually believed I was prepared to live like a monk for the rest of my life?' Saul's voice rose incredulously as he leaned forward to grasp her shaking shoulders.

'I wouldn't have minded if there'd been another woman,' she muttered.

'How very liberated of you!' He watched with a degree of pleasure as she winced beneath his condemnation. Moving his face closer, he enunciated his words with a conciseness that emphasised his rage. 'Let me remind you of something, my sweet little believer. Do you recall St Paul's advice to the Corinthians?' He didn't wait for her answer, and her mind was certainly too numb to supply one. 'He told them that if they couldn't contain themselves they should marry—that it was better to marry than to burn!' The fingers on her shoulders tightened imperceptibly. 'Believe me, I've spent enough of this life in the fires of hell without looking forward to an eternity there!'

CHAPTER NINE

In the savage silence that followed Saul's outburst Penny found herself trying to meet his gaze but flinching away from the agonising emptiness of the eyes that flickered over her still face. In that instant she knew that if the eyes were the windows of the soul she had just been given a glimpse into a lonely and deserted place.

'Besides,' Saul's voice shook with barely controlled emotion, 'I thought I'd already made it clear to you. If we make a home for Lucy it will be one she's proud to bring her friends back to. Don't forget, my angel, it was you who lectured me about my responsibilities! Well, I made a promise to renounce the devil and all his works on Lucy's behalf, and I've no intention of sullying that oath by committing adultery while she's in my care.'

Penny felt the pressure on her shoulders lessen as Saul's fingers followed their gentle slope with a soft caress which had to be a travesty of genuine feeling.

'Especially when I have a wife who has assured me of her total obedience to my demands!'

Dumbly she stared at him, despair mirrored in the depths of her pain-darkened eyes. Saul must have known she wasn't referring to sexual demands when she had made that promise . . . But there was no understanding in the drifting grey gaze as it swept her pallid face with arrogant regard, only a cold contempt tempered with the promise of a fierce retribution should she dare to contest his plans.

'Neither, my pretty Penny, do I intend to let you commit adultery either!' To her burning ears it seemed he reined in his temper with steely self-control. 'So when you want a man in your bed; when you wake up in the early hours of the morning and your warm body's demands override the bleakness of your cold little heart, then it's to me you'll have to come. And if I'm in the mood, then I might provide you with the remedy for your malaise.'

Astonished at his Biblical reference and the depth of passion in his scornful admonishment, Penny fought a losing battle with the inner voice that repeated its call to caution. All the time the man she had married was surprising her with the display of hidden depths to his nature: but one thing they didn't cover was an understanding of the female psyche—something she could remedy that very instant.

'You're crude and ignorant!' She tossed her angry accusation at him. 'Physical desire is nothing to me. Women aren't like men—slaves to their hormones, sexually turned on by attractive bodies or beautiful faces. A woman has to love, to be *in* love, before she's aroused by a man's touch. She has to want him with her mind and heart before she can surrender herself entirely to their mutual conquest and pleasure!'

Her eyes wide and bright with tears above her ashen cheeks, Penny dared him to laugh at her. How could he suppose he could come like a conquering buccaneer out of the blue to plunder her body, just because she had agreed to put on a public act to further his business plans? So all right, at the time he had been under the impression that she was prepared to accept his lovemaking. Now she had told him differently. She looked anxiously for signs of remorse and apology in his expression—and found none.

'You say that as if you really believed it.' Saul's tongue smoothed the outlines of his lips, drawing her attention to the dark slightly swollen tissue. 'And how many men have you been in love with during your short life, I wonder? How many male hands have touched and aroused you like I have tonight?' His breath was coming in great sawing gasps, his control barely held. 'Who were you waiting for on my bed that afternoon? Who was it, Penny . . . or don't you dare to whisper his name to me?'

'No one!' She tried to wriggle away from him, but his arm reached out, pulling her into the threatening power of his body. Cursing her stupidity in not explaining from the very start how innocent her disrobement had been, she willed him to believe her. 'I wasn't waiting for anyone! I——'

'Not anyone? You mean not anyone in particular? Would any man have done for you to add a little spice, a little excitement to the day? Even me, perhaps?' If he saw the horror etched on her face he ignored it. 'Only then I wasn't interested in the *plat du jour*, was I?' Long, sensitive fingers stroked her hair with deceptive gentleness, ran their tips over her shaking shoulders, coming to rest in a parody of love upon the aching centre of one pale breast. 'Only now I'm in France and I'm suddenly very interested . . . very interested indeed . . .'

'I wouldn't willingly have sex with you if you were the last man alive!' Shocked by the venom in his bitter accusations, somehow Penny dredged up the nerve to defy him.

She might still be a virgin at twenty-two, but she had never considered herself either a freak or frigid. With the right man she knew she would be a loving and responsive partner. But the right man was one who would treat her with respect as well as passion, someone who would like her, not just lust after her female body, notching up her possession as a score in some personal table of sexual achievement.

Had Saul treated Tuppy like this? If so it was small wonder she had turned him down, rejecting his atavistic approach that had more of the caveman to it than the suave civilised front he presented to his business colleagues.

'Do you want me to take you by force?' The question came viciously low. 'Is that what all this is about? '

'No . . . oh, no . . .!' Penny was sobbing now, furious with herself for provoking such a threat.

'Because if you do . . .' his deep voice continued slowly, his eyes bottomless pools in the harsh cold beauty of his face, 'I won't oblige you. I'm not averse to bedroom games, but I won't simulate rape for any woman, however desirable she is and however hard she begs me . . .'

'Then let me go!' It was a cry of anguish, wrenched from Penny's heart with all the fervour of a prayer.

Breathlessly, hopelessly she turned her face into the pillow, scarcely able to believe it when she felt Saul's body warmth recede from her.

'Have it your own way, then.' There was a distant arctic coldness in the words that assailed her ears. 'But you might like to think about this . . . either you have me willingly as your husband in the full meaning of the word, or you have nothing, Penny. Nothing at all.'

Her head buried in her arms, her body shaking with sobs, Penny was only vaguely aware he had moved right away and was beginning to dress himself.

Five minutes later she was welcoming the blessed silence that remained after Saul had left the room without speaking another word.

Crawling off the bed, stiff and aching in every limb, she stood for a moment, clasping her arms around her trembling body, trying to rekindle the warmth that Saul's cruel ultimatum had drained away from her.

The only thing she was sure of was that events had moved too fast for her to assimilate and to attempt to come to a decision in her present befuddled state was courting disaster. If only she could be certain of a good night's sleep—surely in the morning she'd be better able to cope . . .

It was then she remembered the sleeping tablets the doctor had prescribed for her after the Mexican disaster. It was ironic that she had never taken one, although at times the temptation to escape the pain of the long lonely nights had been formidable. Only the fear that Lucy might cry out for her had overridden her need for temporary relief from grief in that first terrible week when she was learning to come to terms with her loss.

She expelled her breath in a long-pent-up sigh of misery. Now another woman was looking after her darling Lucy, the man she had married in good faith was threatening all her careful plans and she had nothing at all to keep awake for!

It took only minutes to find the unopened bottle still in her handbag. Gratefully she swallowed the prescribed dose, and by the time she had undressed and showered she was barely awake enough to crawl into the large double bed. Curling herself into a comfortable position as far away from the centre as possible, she fell quickly into a deep dreamless sleep.

It was nine o'clock when she awakened, fighting to keep her eyelids open, pulling herself into consciousness from the drugged sleep. Her head was throbbing, her throat and mouth parched—thanks no doubt to the after-effects of the tablets she had taken, Penny admitted to herself.

She was suddenly conscious of a warm heavy weight on the bed beside her—so Saul had returned! She felt her heart gain pace, thudding against her breastbone with a painful urgency as the events of the previous night flooded back in all their horror. What was she going to say to him? Or even more important—what was he going to say to her! What kind of mood was her rejected bridegroom going to be in after storming out of the bedroom in a fury of frustration?

At least, she accorded bitterly, he wouldn't have had to go far to find someone more willing than she to share his bed, if that had been his purpose. The hotel was only a few minutes away from the infamous Place Pigalle with its night-time entertainment to suit all tastes!

Gingerly, she pulled herself upright, daring to glance down at the body sharing her bed. Thankfully she registered that Saul was still asleep: lying on top of the sheet with the bedspread draped across his lower body. Face relaxed, dark shadow of beard surmounting his jaw, he was more of an unknown quantity than ever. Glad she had been saved the embarrassment of finding him awake, Penny slipped quietly from beneath the sheet and headed for the bathroom.

Splashing her face with cold water, she tried to bring some colour back to her white face and a little of yesterday's sparkle back to her dull eyes. Her enjoyment of the evening had been no sham. During the day she had begun to relax in Saul's company, to warm to him as an intelligent and personable man. There had been real pleasure in being with him, holding his arm, being the recipient of his courteous attention.

Then, when all her defences had been lowered, when she had begun to regard Saul in the role of a friend, he had swooped on her like a Roman soldier on the village of the Sabines and carried her off to slake his own carnal thirst!

Sighing, Penny patted her face dry and began to dress in the aqua trouser and top set she had had the foresight to take into the locked bathroom with her. Dear God, what a dreadful mistake she had made when she'd misunderstood Saul's true intentions about their marriage! She shivered as if someone had trickled ice water down her spine. Last night she had seen a man in the thrall of a barely contained passion—and it had been an awesome sight.

With a practised hand she tried to bring the drawn lines of her face into focus: darkening her brows, lengthening and thickening her long lashes, following the soft curve of her mouth with a subtle shade of pink lipstick. Determined to present a bright face to the man who held her future happiness in his hands despite the trepidation she felt, Penny re-entered the bedroom.

'What's the time?'

It was such a simple everyday question to be greeted with, spoken in a voice still husky with sleep, it took her by surprise.

'Nine o'clock.' Somehow she managed to keep her voice light, wondering what would come next.

Saul's half-shuttered eyes drifted lazily over her

blinking in the light, betraying nothing.

'Were you going out?'

'I'd like to take a few presents back with me.' She'd meant it to sound like a statement, but her voice wavered and even her own ears detected a note of pleading.

To her surprise he nodded. 'Can you find your own way around?'

'Oh, yes!' She tried not to sound too insultingly eager to be rid of his presence. 'My French is quite adequate and I've got all the maps I need.'

She waited with bated breath for Saul's approval, and received it without delay.

'As long as you're back at the hotel by four-thirty in time to pack and leave for the airport I've no objection.'

Stopping only to collect her handbag, Penny closed the bedroom door behind her, a deep sigh of relief escaping her soft mouth. No anger, no recriminations, just the impersonal reaction of a man who knew he held all the trumps.

The next few hours passed quickly as Penny wandered through the busy Paris streets, her mind intent on shopping.

By midday she was thankful to sink down at a table in an open-air café in Montmartre to order herself a *café crème*, carefully stowing her small collection of parcels beneath the table: amongst them a pale lemon stretch suit for Lucy for immediate wear and a gorgeous party dress that would fit her in another year's time. It was her pledge to the future—a personal declaration of her own purpose to win and keep her sister's daughter.

'*Merci*.' she nodded her thanks to the waiter as the fragrant cup was placed before her.

Stirring the dark liquid, she watched the cream swirl

into concentric circles. There was no doubt in her mind that Saul had raised no objections to her solitary excursion because he recognised her need to get things into perspective. If she had ever harboured any hope that he would change his mind and revert to her original plan of a non-consummated marriage, that hope was now dead. He had been coolly civilised in his attitude towards her that morning. But she knew that behind the veneer of culture his adamantine spirit was as determined as ever to insist on his own terms.

She shuddered, impulsively reaching down to her feet to open the bag containing Lucy's dress. Staring down at its delicate embroidery, she knew she had to reach a decision—and fast. It was a chastening thought to realise that Saul preferred the idea of Lucy being fostered to her being left in the sole care of her only aunt!

Was letting Saul have sovereignty over her body too dreadful a sacrifice to contemplate when the rewards would be so great? Wouldn't the joy of loving and caring for Lucy outweigh the price she was being asked to pay? Besides, she admitted reluctantly, Saul was an intensely attractive man in a physical sense. Even in the trauma of the previous night she had realised she was being torn two ways—her heart and mind crying out for a man who could love and respect her; her body coming to life for Saul, responding with a demeaning abandonment to the sight, the scent, the taste of him.

Slowly she sipped her coffee. Last night she had pulled herself back from the brink of that mindless surrender, frightened by the strength and violence she had sensed in her husband's powerful body, and the depth of the desire that had put him beyond the reach of logical argument. From the ardency of his caresses she had known he expected her to be capable of a full and instant response—and she hadn't been. Her untried body would have disappointed him and humiliated her. Sadly she had to admit the truth.

From their disastrous first meeting Saul had carried a false and contemptuous opinion of her which she had been too embarrassed and proud to correct. Originally it hadn't been important, because she had resolved never to see him again!

Later, in comparison with the Mexican tragedy, it had seemed trivial and inconsequential. Now she could see what a bad mistake it had been not to put the record right when she had bearded Saul in his den! Thoughtfully she finished her coffee and replaced the cup in the saucer. As things stood at present it might be an equally bad decision to admit her innocence.

Saul might despise what he saw as her free-and-easy attitude towards casual sexual encounters, but he wanted to partake of those favours. There was no guarantee he would view a virgin bride as a desirable acquisition!

Determined not to give Saul cause for adverse comment, Penny made sure she was back at the hotel with time to spare.

Only two days since she had kissed Lucy goodbye and already she was experiencing the pangs of separation, as painful as if Lucy had been her own child. On an impulse she made for one of the telephone kiosks reserved for guests. Now international dialling was so easy why not call up Margaret and ask how things were? In her present state of mind to hear a friendly voice would be a tonic!

'Penny? Good heavens! Is anything wrong?' Margaret's voice sounded more concerned than friendly.

'No, of course not!' Penny hastened to reassure the

other woman. There was a good deal wrong, but not in any sense she could disclose to Margaret. 'I had a few moments to spare before we leave and I just wondered how everything was your end.'

'Oh, I'm coping quite well.' Margaret's dry response gave way to soft laughter. 'My dear girl, Lucy's fine. I hope you haven't been worrying yourself about her needlessly and spoiling your honeymoon.'

How could one spoil a disaster? Penny bit her lip. 'Not really,' she excused herself.

'Now you listen to me, my dear,' Margaret's voice echoed the growing affection she felt for her charge's young aunt. 'You make the most of having your lovely new husband to yourself while you can. You'll have enough disruptions in the future! I know how much you want to be with Lucy, but take my advice, share your love if you must, but never let Saul take second place. Second place is no position for a man like the one you've married!'

Too touched by Margaret's genuine understanding to be offended at the small lecture, Penny clasped the receiver more tightly.

'I guess I'm still worried in case the court won't give me guardianship,' she confessed unhappily.

'Then you're worrying needlessly.' Margaret's voice, firm and experienced, was just the support she needed. 'Even a fool could see that you and your husband will make a splendid family for her. And believe me, the court is no fool.'

'Yes, I suppose so.' Penny felt a stab of fear at the remark that was meant to be reassuring. If the court was no fool it might discern that things were far from what they should be between her and Saul. Only by being anything and everything he wanted would she be able to win the full support she so desperately needed. She forced herself to speak cheerfully. 'Give her my love and tell her I'll try to come and see her tomorrow.'

Of course Lucy wouldn't understand the message, but she would appreciate the kiss and cuddle that would accompany it. Already the little girl was showing the warm sunny nature that had made her mother irresistible. It was a thought that made Penny smile as she replaced the receiver and turned to find herself face to face with Saul.

'Well, what's all this?' He smiled a hard tight smile that didn't reach his eyes. 'Friends in France? Or may one enquire what matter of urgency compelled you to phone England? Some discarded lover, maybe, who thought he might be resuming his relationship when you returned?'

'If it was,' she retorted crisply, refusing to treat his sniping seriously, 'he now knows differently.'

'Really?' Anxious to gain the lift, Penny found the tall hard body of her husband squarely blocking her way. 'That was a very wise move on your part, my darling. Does that mean you're prepared to honour your marriage vows in their entirety now?'

There was a quality about Saul as he stood there with one eyebrow raised quizzically that she couldn't define. Part of her was afraid of him, of the threat he posed to her independence and her rights over her own body, but another part of her was responding with a tingling warmth to his very male magnetism. Almost as if he sensed her dilemma he allowed his eyes to drift over her with obvious appreciation as he awaited her reply. 'Well?' he prompted softly.

It wasn't the place or time she would have chosen, but

since she had no option but to surrender, perhaps it was just as well it was in such a public place, she thought grimly. And if Saul expected docility or sweetness from her in his moment of triumph he would be disappointed.

'It means I'm prepared to do whatever is necessary to ensure that I have your full support when I go to court,' she told him coldly.

The harshness of her words wiped the half-smile from his expectant face as the next moment she found her arm seized and firmly held. 'Whatever . . . and however, my love,' Saul's dark face so near her own was tight with displeasure, his voice low and passionate, 'I like my women to smile when I make love to them . . . to look as if they're enjoying it, not just accepting me on sufferance. Is that clear?'

'Saul . . .' Penny protested, wild eyes glancing around to see if people were watching them. 'Saul . . . please . . .'

'No, my darling.' Fierce and low his tone as his grip on her arm tightened. 'You're the one who has to please, not me.' He gave a short bark of laughter. 'You shouldn't find that too difficult. If you can't bear to look at me when you do it, just close your eyes and pretend I'm someone else. That shouldn't be beyond you, with all the experience you've had.'

'What a clever solution!' She almost hissed the words at him, angry and hurt by the edge of scorn in his condemnation. 'And of course you can do the same.' Eyes bright with fury, shoulders thrust back, she cast discretion to the winds. 'Which of your lovers am I most like . . . Samantha? Or someone more recent? T . . .'

Her sister's name never left her tongue as Saul closed her mouth by the simple expedient of sealing it with his own hard, angry lips. She could feel his whole body trembling as he pushed her back against the wall, trapping her there with its weight while he took his toll from her. Vainly trying to control her panic and mortified by the public display Saul was subjecting her to, Penny made no attempt to ward him off.

But it seemed her very passivity was a challenge to his manhood. The broadness of his body masking the passage of his hands, he deliberately slid his palms beneath her sweater, riding the smooth skin of her back to find and unloose the clasp of her bra, following its forward fall to entrap her bared breasts between the forks of thumbs and forefingers.

'Is this what you like, Penny?' Her mouth was released so he could whisper the question against her ear. 'Does it give you a thrill to be made love to in a crowd? Are you excited in case I lose control and carry you into the public lounge and ravish you before an audience? Is that what you'd like, my angel?'

Penny felt the tremor that surged through his body; saw the dark agony on his face and suddenly understood. Samantha! His wife had enjoyed the kind of gratification Saul had described to her, and he thought they were two of a kind. No wonder he had reacted so violently to the sight of her that afternoon when he'd found her in a state of undress in his room. He'd judged her on a painful precedent not of her own making!

How could she explain how terribly mistaken he was now? All she could do was play for time and hope the opportunity for explanation would come within the next few days, to calm him down before she suffered too great a humiliation at his hands.

'You're confusing me with someone else,' she asserted quietly. 'Personally, I find all public displays of emotion nauseous.' She swallowed to stop her voice trembling. 'And now, if you'll get out of my way, I have to pack.'

Without flinching she met the angry grey eyes that passed searchingly from her own steady gaze to the bruised contours of her delicate mouth and on to where her breasts rose and fell in a rapid motion, betraying her distress.

'You have one hour before we leave.'

Saul stepped back and she was free. Walking with a fierce pride, not looking back at where he stood, Penny entered the lift.

Thankfully she relaxed against its padded walls, glad she was the only occupant. Her legs were weak, her arms trembling. Dear God, if she'd known she was destined to bear the punishment merited by the meretricious Samantha would she have entered into this contract of marriage with Saul van Diemen?

She already knew the answer. If Lucy's future was at stake she would have bedded down with the devil himself.

CHAPTER TEN

THE WEATHER in England was damp and cold: a far cry from the late autumn sunshine of Paris. Saul's beautiful country house standing in two acres of land felt cold and cheerless as Penny crossed the threshold for the first time as his wife.

It was easy for her to imagine how he must have felt returning to it alone after his business trips abroad. Yet would being with her on this occasion make his homecoming more pleasurable? The journey from Paris had been undertaken with as little conversation between them as possible, each indulging in the polite platitudes that circumstances demanded. It was hardly an auspicious beginning to the years that lay ahead!

Casting her eyes round the spacious hall, Penny felt distinctly nervous at the prospect of being thrust into the deep end. Not only had she to determine some routine for managing the large five-bedroomed house as well as caring for Lucy, but unexpectedly she was going to have to accept Saul as her lover, submit to the attentions of a man who despised her, whom to all intents and purposes she had blackmailed into marrying her! How different it would have been if he had some feeling for her, she thought, her heart sinking at the prospect. The worst thing was that his need for her wasn't even based on liking or even honest desire!

She watched gloomily as Saul dumped the suitcases in the hallway before following him into what she remem-

bered as being the large sitting-room which had been the
focal point of Lucy's christening party.

Her eyes, dwelling on his athletic frame, admired the
broad shoulders and tapered torso, the long, muscled legs
barely disguised by the elegant cut of his suit . . . his
wedding suit. A stab of pity troubled her tender heart.
How badly Samantha must have hurt him to make his
attitude so sour towards her sex! She fought back the
ready tears that compassion had fed to her solemn eyes.
Perhaps if Saul hadn't suffered so often from the pain of
lost love he wouldn't have become so warped towards the
female gender. To be loved was the ultimate joy a woman
could experience . . . to be lusted after was understand-
able, but to be treated as merely therapeutic and
abhorred at the same time was unbearable. It made her
like a dose of nasty medicine . . . unpleasant but
unavoidable to achieve salvation.

Would Saul expect to claim his rights tonight? The
thought brought a clammy coldness to discomfit her. If so
she would have to hide her torment, for hadn't he told her
he expected willingness, not forbearance? She would
have to follow his cynical suggestion . . . shut her eyes
and think of someone else. Only it wouldn't be another
man's image that would fill her mind . . . it would be
Lucy's enchanting face that would help her through the
ordeal. Lucy, whose needs were paramount.

Despite her resolve Penny found it impossible to
repress the shiver that convulsed her slim frame.

'Cold?'

Saul's query showed her shudder of discomfort had
been witnessed.

Instinctively she turned her head away in case his swift
assessment discovered something in her face she would

prefer him not to see.

'Don't worry,' he said brusquely when she didn't answer, as if her silence condemned him, 'I'll switch on the central heating and there's an electric fire to give spot heating. In ten minutes you'll find the room quite habitable. At least,' he added drily, 'as far as the temperature is concerned.'

'Perhaps I can get us something to eat?' Penny suggested diffidently. She might just as well get started on her household duties, and to be out of Saul's disturbing presence would give her a chance to bring her turbulent emotions under control.

'Why not?' came the laconic reply. 'Liz has a key and promised to stock the fridge and freezer ready for our return. See what you can find.'

Something quick and appetising, Penny determined, having located the kitchen from memory, finding herself duly impressed with the array of cooking utensils. Had Saul been used to having live-in girlfriends to cook for him? If so, he had probably been disappointed at their lack of culinary skill, because many items appeared unused, she registered with amusement. Either that, or he had had Liz buy them especially for his new housekeeper.

Still, she consoled herself with a small grimace of resignation, since she found most creative pursuits a joy she would certainly see he wasn't disappointed in his future cuisine! Tonight, however, it was a time for compromise.

Liz had certainly fulfilled her commission well, she mused, deciding eventually on egg, bacon, chips and baked beans. Hardly a gourmet offering, she admitted, presenting it with some trepidation, relieved when Saul ate without comment but with obvious enjoyment.

How tired and strained his face appeared in the soft light. Putting down her empty plate, she studied him with concern. But then he had had little sleep the previous night. Vivid recollections of the Place Pigalle with its gaudy neon signs, explicit video shows and live entertainment flashed through her brain. A tiny moan of remorse escaped her throat as she remembered Saul's furious departure and the nature of the solace she might have driven him to seek.

'What's the matter?' It was no more than a polite question spoken in his deep impersonal voice, yet it scythed through her with the sharp agony of a blade.

Conscious that she was clasping her hands nervously but unable to control their spasmodic movements, Penny found it impossible to admit to the unasked-for concern she felt for his well being.

'Nothing,' she stumbled over the sentence, praying for inspiration, 'it's just that—just that it's been a very exhausting day.' She pushed her hair away from her face in a gesture that betrayed her nervousness.

'I'm sorry, I'm being inconsiderate.' Saul hauled himself to his feet with the polished courtesy of a complete stranger acting host. 'I'll take you up to your room.' He stood there patiently.

Dumbly Penny rose to her feet, taking a deep breath in an effort to calm the racing beat of her heart. In the hallway he paused to gather up her case before silently indicating that she follow him up the gracious staircase.

The room he took her to was beside the one she knew to her cost to be his own. As he stood back to allow her to enter, Penny had an impression of a rose and fawn décor, a large bed with a luxurious duvet cover flung over it, fitted furniture and two elegant little bedroom chairs covered in rose velvet.

'Oh, it's lovely, Saul!' Her cry of pleasure was spontaneous.

'I'm delighted it meets with your approval.' The smile he turned on her was faintly cynical. 'It was my intention to make your prison as comfortable as possible.'

Despite the curl of his mouth Penny detected a certain wryness in the admission, almost as if he were making a tentative apology for the misapprehension which had devastated her.

'No bread and water?' she returned lightly. Comfortable indeed! Luxurious would have been a better adjective. She saw the grim lines of his face soften at her quip, the cruel mouth grow oddly tender, and alarmingly she felt herself the victim of a strange warm sensation starting inside her and spreading its disquieting tentacles through her limbs. Her gaze, caught to Saul's, could not escape his powerful regard.

'I'll make you an allowance for the household budget automatically topped up from my own account. How you spend it is up to you—within reason.' There was a devilish mockery in his startlingly beautiful eyes. 'Smoked salmon and wine . . . or bread and water . . . you may choose the fare that pleases you best.'

A vivid excitement was following in the wake of the heated wave that surged through her veins as Penny lifted her head erect, holding and interpreting his penetrating appraisal. The words were symbolic. Saul was telling her she was the mistress of her own fate within the environment she had chosen for herself. He was inviting her to make a heaven out of the hell she had walked so blindly into.

'Saul ...' She breathed his name, a heavy pulse beating in her throat as she felt an almost uncontrollable longing to put her arms round his neck, to draw him close, to whisper that she was not the wanton he supposed her to be. She wanted to tell him he would be the first man to possess her, to exhort him to be gentle with her, to teach her before he took her ... She wanted to tell him to pull down the barrier of distrust between them because she would go to him willingly ... not for Lucy's sake, but for his.

Already on his way towards the door having torn himself away from her beseeching eyes, Saul paused as his name trembled on her tongue.

'S-Saul ...' Penny stammered painfully, running the tip of her tongue over lips that quivered, unable to voice the muddled, inexplicable emotions that churned within her.

'Yes?' One dark eyebrow raised, he waited patiently framed against the doorway, poised to leave, his head bare inches from the top lintel.

'I ... I ...' she stumbled miserably, pinned to the spot by his unnerving stare, feeling the blood rising to her cheeks as she hunted for the words to express feelings she hadn't even begun to come to terms with.

'It's all right, Penny.' There was dry resignation in his even tone as he drifted his gaze over her pleading face, dwelling briefly on her tear-sparkled eyes, her hesitant lips, the rapid rise and fall of her breasts before ending on the twisting tortured fingers clasped at her waist. 'There's no key in the lock—but you'll have no need of one. I promise I shan't disturb you. Sleep well.'

The door closed behind him and she was left staring at its blank face, her heart pitching a furious rhythm as the adrenalin raced through her blood. Primed for the action she had failed to take, she felt like screaming!

Two hours later she was still awake, imbued with the sure knowledge that she was destined at this rate to count every tick of the little bedside clock until it was morning, or she went mad—whichever happened first.

It was then she remembered the washing-up. Heavens, what had possessed her? She had left Saul's spotless kitchen in one hell of a mess! If she'd been trying to aggravate him she could hardly have made a worse start. All that fat congealing in his new frying pan! She shuddered at her own slovenliness. Thank God she'd realised in time to do something about it.

Walking carefully down the darkened stairs, she blessed the efficiency of the central heating. Used to more substantial nightwear than Liz's idea of bedtime glamour, she didn't possess a dressing-gown and she hadn't thought to put a jacket on. Still, she comforted herself, the house wasn't overlooked, and if she did start to feel chilly she'd have her hands in hot water.

'What the hell . . .!'

Her hand on the kitchen door, Penny turned, trapped in a sudden blaze of light as the deep masculine voice accosted her. Like a moth surprised by a torch she stood transfixed, blinking as her distended pupils struggled to adapt themselves to the sudden influx of light.

Saul's face was a comic mixture of shock and irritation, as if she had been caught trying to steal the silver, she thought with an inward curl of laughter. His dark hair was tousled as if he'd been running his fingers through it, and from his appearance it seemed he'd had difficulty in sleeping too.

Gone was the smart suit he had travelled in. As her

eyes grew accustomed to the brightness of the hall light she was able to discern that in fact all he was wearing was a very short, multi-coloured towelling bathrobe. In his hand was what appeared to be a glass of Scotch not overly diluted with a mixer, if its deep golden tone was any indication.

Swallowing in embarrassment, Penny cleared her throat. 'I didn't mean to disturb you. I was going to do the washing up.'

Saul looked at her as if she'd gone mad.

'At two o'clock in the morning?'

'I forgot all about it earlier . . . and I couldn't sleep anyway,' she explained, uncomfortably aware of the picture she must be making, like a gaudy specimen pinned to a card.

'Neither could I.' Saul gestured down to the glass in his hand. 'I think you might find this a better remedy than washing up, my pretty Penny.'

'Yes . . .' She dared hardly breathe. His voice had softened. Had she even caught a trace of affection as he spoke her name? 'Perhaps a very small one, then,' she agreed tremulously.

Wordlessly Saul beckoned her to enter the sitting-room, switching off the bright hall light as she obeyed.

Inside the room she was plunged back into a dim softness of illumination, the flicker from the fire, a discreet well-shaded table lamp.

Watching her own reflection in the mirror as Saul poured out a drink for her, she saw what he would see when he looked at her. A young woman whose hair gleamed a dark russet round an oval face, the eyes of which were dark and smudged beneath the finely drawn brows: the mouth a warm pink invitation to the lips of a man seeking consolation. Reflected light gleamed on the proud slopes of her high rounded breasts, spun its magic touch on the soft contours of her silk-covered abdomen, highlighted the long shapely legs, their skin gleaming through the lace-decorated slits that rose from floor level to her waist, turning her into the image of a seductress.

Slowly Saul put both glasses down on the cabinet and walked across the room towards her, his eyes boring like steel gimlets as time seemed to stand still.

The shadow of his eyelashes cast wedges of darkness on his strong cheekbones. In the half-light he seemed immensely powerful, almost godlike. Penny caught her breath as her heart thundered and she felt a primeval inexplicable urge to surrender abjectly before such total uncompromising male majesty.

Shaken by the depth of her response, when Saul raised a lazy hand to finger but not disturb one slender strap on her shoulder she felt herself flinch, with a heady anticipation, not fear.

'Why did you really come downstairs?' Deep, clotted with a tremulous passion, the question was scarcely more than a whisper. Penny shivered, feeling her legs grow weak, praying there wouldn't be an inquest on her reply . . . that Saul would accept it at its face value.

'I wanted you.'

Clear but low, the words seemed to linger on the air as Saul let out a long trembling sigh.

'Are you sure?' This time his fingers were more daring, sliding each strap in turn from her shoulders, palming the top of her nightdress lower so that it rolled away from her body, exposing her breasts pale and perfect to his avid gaze.

'Yes!' Penny gasped the monosyllable, pulsatingly

aware that suddenly it was true by its own virtue. She could feel his body warmth, sense the excitement that was coursing through his veins, and it was arousing a deep-core response in her own heated flesh. Lucy or no, she wanted to yield the sovereignty of her body to the care of this overpowering alien who was her husband.

She gave a small inarticulate cry as Saul lowered his head, his arms supporting her naked back, to trace a long, lingering kiss across the tip of each of her breasts in turn, feeling each cherished apex tauten and tingle beneath his hungry mouth.

She made no move to prevent him when he pushed the nightdress even further downward, kneeling before her like a pilgrim at a shrine to follow its gradual descent to her waist with a stream of kisses that seemed to turn her whole body to jelly and atrophy her mind.

Penny was shocked yet filled with an extraordinary excitement at the yearning tenderness of Saul's gentle salute. Whether her knees buckled or the sudden surge of his arms round her lower body made her lose balance she would never know. Letting out a low anguished cry as his lips adored her, she found herself subsiding on the soft carpet with Saul as her master gentling her bared flesh with eager hands, his mouth pressing tender tributes on her mouth, her eyes, her cheeks, tracing the warm satin stretch of her slender neck.

Her pulses were jumping and there was a strange tremulous ache deep inside her as Saul disengaged himself from her embrace. She watched spellbound as he shed his robe, saw the glow from the fire shine warm on the naked skin of golden shoulders, lay its gleam on hard ribs and highlight strongly muscled thighs. She could feel her own uncovered skin pulsating with the warmth of the fire as he leaned over her, proudly, magnificently naked, totally and beautifully male.

An elemental need was growing inside her, absorbing her trepidation, speeding with the power of an electric current, sending its heated messages to every cell of her eager sensititive skin, as Saul returned to her.

With sure hands and avid mouth he loved her, worshipping her flesh, uttering small disjointed phrases of wonder and admiration, breathing a barely audible lover's litany of verbal seduction.

And Penny knew she was being seduced, welcoming the spreading heat within her, feeling it devour any trace of rigidity as she moved with sweet generous abandon, offering herself without reservation to his demands and her own delight.

Miraculously his body joined with hers with no awkwardness, no pain, just a sensation of total inevitability, as if it had been what she had been waiting for all her life.

Images from their days together as man and wife flickered on the screen of her mind, and before that, memories of their first meeting ... the moment of introduction when Saul had held out his hand in formal greeting and clasped her own ... his cool, firm handshake ... the tantalising smile ... the initial shock when she had first met the full battery from those mocking, inscrutable eyes.

Nothing was as it had been. With the rupturing of the flimsy physical barrier that had guarded her virginity had come the stupendous realisation that she loved Saul.

The truth was blindingly clear—impossible to discount. The cold blood in which she had married him had turned into a red-hot stream that fired every nerve and cell she had. Not because of what had just happened between them. That soaring act of passion had served only to tear down the barriers of her own blindness.

Now she could see that the magnetism had been there from the start. Instinctively she had sensed that Saul was a dangerous threat to her equilibrium and just as mindlessly she had raised a shield of indifference to protect herself.

Intuitively she had fought him, squaring up to his hostility instead of laughing off the ridiculous scene in his bedroom on the afternoon of the party. Afterwards grief, pain and despair had taken their toll of her common sense as well as her courtesy.

It hadn't been easy to haul down her flag of independence that day when she had dared to visit him in his office to tell him where his duty lay. In retrospect she could see how well she had deserved the rough ride he had given her.

Yet despite her autocratic approach he had swallowed her insults, overlooked her angry attestations and come to her rescue.

Penny found it impossible to stop weeping as she forced herself to recognise her true feelings towards the man who was kneeling at her side, stroking her hair back from her damp face with caring fingers, while she sobbed out the healing tears into the towelling robe he had dragged on across his own satiated body.

She didn't know the precise moment she had fallen in love. Too busy putting up barriers against the powerful physical attraction Saul had exercised over her, she hadn't allowed herself to register the finer points of his nature. But they had been there all the time to see—his tenderness with Lucy, his charm and good nature on that wonderful day in Paris.

For the first time, with the veils peeled from her eyes, Penny realised the strength of the unconscious signals she had been transmitting to him the evening they had spent at the nightclub.

Her face burnt with mortification as she buried it against the rough towelling. No wonder he had assumed she wanted him to make love to her! On that evening Saul had read her needs and desires more accurately than she herself!

Then on top of all that, to have misunderstood him so completely when he had spoken of separate rooms! No wonder he had been so furious with her, tossing out his angry ultimatum before striding out into the night to cool his own frustrations. A shudder convulsed her as she was forced to recognise how a lesser man than Saul might have reacted to that situation.

She made a deep inarticulate noise in her throat as she accepted the outcome of her self-revelation.

She loved her husband to distraction—and the healing balm of that love was going to make the painful soreness of Tuppy's loss more easy to bear.

She was no longer alone. Saul had impregnated her with his strength and his fortitude.

Before she realised what was happening, she was being lifted in his arms, her own arms wound round his neck, her face nestled against his sweet skin, savouring the dampness that lay in moist drops against his hair and neck.

She wanted to speak, to tell him of her marvellous discovery. As he carried her up the stairs she tried to find the words to explain, but she felt so warm and lethargic— and after all, they would have all the night together to exchange such delicious pillow talk . . .

It was to her room Saul took her, laying her gently beneath the duvet, his face tightening when she gave a little yelp of discomfort as her spine protested—its bones bruised by her uninhibited movements on the hard floor. But she stirred voluptuously as he leaned down to brush his lips against her forehead, smoothing a wing of deep auburn hair from her warm damp cheek.

For a moment he stayed staring down at her, his jaw taut, the brightness of his compelling eyes clouded with some unexpressed emotion. She half expected him to speak . . . say her name with affection. A slight frown marred her brow. Never once in all that wonderful act of love had he called her by her name . . . Then he was straightening up, still silent, and she watched from beneath heavy lashes as he uncurled his long body, wanting to see him discard his robe, to feast her eyes on his male beauty before he joined her.

Even when he walked to the door she still believed it was only to put the light out: was still anticipating the pleasure of spending her first night cuddled against his demanding strength. Then she saw the door open . . . and close . . . and she was all alone.

CHAPTER ELEVEN

SEPARATE rooms, Saul had said. Separate rooms so we don't have to spend the whole night with each other if we don't want to. He couldn't have made it any clearer how little affected he had been by what had just happened between them.

Sick with disappointment, Penny sank back on the soft pillow. In her fevered imagination she had fantasised that in her arms Saul had undergone a similar revelation to her own: that a dormant feeling for her had burst into unexpected life.

She had made the basic female mistake of believing he couldn't have made love to her with that wonderful combination of power, passion and tenderness if his feelings hadn't echoed the depth of her own.

Sadder and wiser, she lay for a long time, frightened by the intensity of her newly discovered feelings for her uninterested husband.

Hours later the sound of the door opening roused her from a sleep troubled by dark and distressing dreams. Struggling into a sitting position, grimacing as her spinal cord protested once more about what she had subjected it to the previous evening, Penny pushed her tumbled hair away from her face, controlling an absurd desire to cover her half-naked breasts as she saw Saul's unsmiling eyes linger on their pale swell beneath the transparent nightdress. Such an action would be ludicrous since he knew her so intimately.

Stoically she accepted the steady appraising gaze of his darkened eyes, her own face lengthening in dismay as she realised she was being served breakfast in bed—orange juice, toast and coffee.

'Thank you very much.' She took the tray across her knees. 'But this is all wrong. I mean . . . I should have been the one to get up and get your breakfast.'

She groaned, remembering the washing-up she'd been prevented from doing.

Saul's smile was faint, a mere twist of his mouth, but it lessened the severity of his hard-boned face.

'It's still very early. I want to get to the office and start work on the Middle East project as soon as possible. There's no reason why you can't have a lie-in for a few mornings. You won't get many when Lucy arrives.'

There was something infuriating about his cool efficiency. The breakfast had been carefully prepared and served, but how much more she would have preferred it if Saul had come in empty-handed, taken her in his arms, wrapped his lithe body round her and plastered her unresisting flesh with kisses! Damn her sentimental pipe dreams! Angrily she shifted her body, her face wincing momentarily as her back stabbed its displeasure.

What a fool she was being. Saul had never pretended to like her—let alone love her!

Furious with herself, she expended her wrath on him. 'When will that be, do you suppose? Will I have to finish a probationary period first to please you? Prove I can fulfil every part of our agreement—wash, clean, cook, entertain?' She paused, her breath sawing with suppressed passion, her breast heaving with emotion.

Watching Saul's lean jaw tighten at her outburst, she

hated herself for what she was doing. Yet, driven on by some inner demon, she couldn't control the need to inflict still more pain on herself.

'I hope I was satisfactory last night?'

'Very commendable.' Saul's level voice was toneless, his face pale and set as he stared down at her tear-bright eyes, her provocatively raised chin. 'But don't worry, you won't be asked to repeat the performance.'

Her breath caught in her throat at the finality of the terse statement. 'But . . .'

Miserably she stared down at the neat triangles of toast as if mesmerised by them. Why now, when she would gladly have given him anything and everything he wanted, was Saul rejecting her? 'I don't understand,' she muttered at last, her powers of argument defeated by the way he had withdrawn from her.

'There's not much to understand.' He spoke harshly, his voice reflecting the taut anguish of his face, as he stared down at her puzzled expression. 'I've decided to accept the terms you originally offered me—although I still insist on a permanent arrangement for the child's sake. You've got your own way, Penny. If it's any consolation to you, last night was as painful to me as it was for you.'

Painful! Penny flinched at his cruelty. Last night he had taken her to heights she had never dreamed of. How could he dismiss their lovemaking in such scathing terms?

'Saul . . . please . . .' Her mind in a turmoil, she thrust the tray away from her, swinging her legs out of bed to catch hold of his arm as he turned to leave. 'Don't go, don't walk out on me like this!'

'I have to leave.' His answer was brusque to the point

of rudeness as his hands seized her wrists and pushed her away from him. Losing balance, she toppled back on to the bed, her face ashen. 'There's no need for alarm—my decision makes no difference to your plans. I intend to see my solicitor today about making an application for guardianship.'

He glanced down quickly at his watch. 'I expect you'll be able to amuse yourself in my absence—make yourself familiar with the house, sort out the tools of your trade.' His smile was perfunctory. 'You'll see the room next to this has been turned into a nursery and across the hallway another bedroom has been made into a studio for you.'

'Thank you.' Penny answered him through dry lips, watching with pain-dazed eyes as he walked away from her.

Only the knowledge that her fight for Lucy was making progress gave her any consolation that morning as she spent it exploring her new domain as Saul had suggested, familiarising herself with the layout and making mental notes for arranging a work-schedule for the coming days.

After a light lunch of omelette and bread and butter she settled down to organising the room Saul had designated as her studio. If only she'd felt more cheerful she would have been overjoyed at the way he had catered to her wildest expectations. From the extensive working surface with its storage cupboards to the display shelves round the magnolia-painted walls, the room was everything she had ever dreamed of. As it was, her joy was tempered with the deep depression her early morning encounter with Saul had left hanging over her.

Wearily she put her hand to the small of her back. All the pulling about of crates certainly hadn't helped her sore bones, she admitted ruefully as with a small sigh she sank down in the comfortable armchair that Saul in his wisdom must have provided for just such moments of stress.

It was then her eyes alighted on the small cardboard box containing the personal odds and ends she had collected from Tuppy's flat, amongst them the little red-bound diary that had disclosed her twin's love affair with Saul.

How long ago had her sister lain in Saul's arms, felt the strength and power of his body? she wondered, fruitlessly attempting to deny the twinge of envy she felt. A frown grooved her forehead. Her grief had been so raw, her despair so absolute that dreadful day she had opened the little book, praying for some miracle to lead her in the right direction, and she had been so stunned by the revelation afforded to her, she hadn't even looked at the date! At the time, the facts had been enough to send her speeding to Saul van Diemen for help.

Now as a pang of very real jealousy twisted her heart she wanted to know just how recently it was that her husband had begged her beautiful twin sister to be his wife.

Placating her conscience by reminding herself that Tuppy had always shared her secrets with her, she lifted the diary from the box.

There it was, the simple sentence that was like a knife thrust in her heart: 'Saul begged me to reconsider marriage'. And the month? Penny uttered a low cry of dismay. August!

The room seemed to darken as she fought the faint that would have put a momentary stop to her agony. In August Tuppy had been four months pregnant . . . and

Saul had begged her to marry him!

She forced herself to turn the pages back, knowing what she would find—and yes, there it was! April. It was in April that Tuppy had confessed to being in Saul's bed . . . the April that Lucy had been conceived.

Saul was Lucy's father. How could she interpret the facts otherwise? Yet her sister, who had been living with Michael at the time, had chosen to marry the man she loved rather than the man with whom she had had a brief affair. After months of heart-searching after she had found out she was pregnant, Tuppy had turned down Saul's proposal, giving him the consolation prize of being godfather to his own baby!

A harsh dry sob escaped Penny's throat. Dear God, how Saul must have suffered after Tuppy's death, knowing he could never make a valid claim to his own flesh and blood. How helpless and furious he must have felt when she, Penny, had taken full responsibility, refusing him any knowledge of or access to her niece. And what a shock it must have been when she walked into his office and announced that she wanted him to marry her and give a home to Lucy on a temporary basis!

Little wonder he had given full rein to his scorn before presenting her with his revised plan. Now she could see why he wanted to bind her to him with the strongest ties the law gave him. Why, last night, he had made certain she would have no grounds for annulment, and why having achieved his aim he had no further interest in her.

Saul still loved her sister, the mother of his child. She didn't want to believe it, but all the evidence was there. Last night had been 'painful' for him. Last night he had closed his eyes in the dimness of the firelit room, listened to her voice repeating his name and imagined it was her sister he was holding in his arms once more, adoring with his mouth, conquering with every powerful surge of his body . . .

Penny moaned aloud as the realisation chilled her blood. She could never emulate Tuppy. She would never have her sister's beauty, her vivacity, her flair for enjoying life. All she could ever be was an agonising reminder of what Saul had lost, tolerated in his house because she had given him the one thing her sister had refused—the custody of his own child.

Sick with shock, Penny closed the diary. It had been a well kept secret. Certainly Michael could never have known, and Tuppy, who had in the past confided all things to her twin sister, had on this occasion kept her own counsel.

Knowing Tuppy as she had, Penny could imagine the torture her sister must have gone through before making her final decision.

No wonder she had waited so long into her pregnancy before agreeing to marry. And Saul? Saul, who had already lost so much, must have resigned himself to yet another deprivation until she, Penny, had burst into his life, innocently offering him what was his own kith and kin!

He had deliberately concealed the secret buried so deeply in his heart, and it seemed unlikely he would reveal it to her at this late date, unless . . . a spasm of fear made her tremble. Did he intend to wait until after the court's decision and then spring the facts on her? Would he delay the news until she had won her fight for guardianship and then let her know the real reason he had agreed to marry her—the reasoning behind his insistence on their union being consummated?

What a fool she had been to imagine for one moment that Saul cared anything for her, let alone had come to love her!

Dully she rose to her feet. She could only hazard a guess at his silence on the matter. Loyalty to her sister's memory—fear that perhaps if she did know the truth she would love Lucy the less, be less prepared to plead for her custody?

If it was the latter it just showed how little Saul really knew her. Not only was Lucy Tuppy's daughter, she was also part of Penny's life. She loved the little girl and that was that. To her mind love didn't have qualifications dependent on circumstances. It was an absolute emotion. She loved Lucy and she loved Saul. Despite what she had discovered, she was still going to try and do her best for both of them—if they would let her.

Like a zombie she managed to get through the rest of the day, deciding when she had cleared up after her lunch to explore the neighbourhood. A leisurely stroll from the house brought her to a bus stop, and from there it was a short ride to the nearest small town, where she spent her time window-shopping, mingling with the crowds of housewives, some of them pushing young children around in baby buggies.

Soon she would be doing likewise, she assured herself. The alternative was too dreadful to contemplate.

Attracted to a large supermarket, she bought a piece of fillet steak, mushrooms and onion rings in batter as well as a glamorous-looking gâteau before treating herself to a cup of coffee and making tracks for home.

Home, she thought ironically, her mouth twisting into a rueful smile, Saul's lovely house was still far from being a home as far as she was concerned. While the coolness between herself and the man she had persuaded to marry her lasted there was small chance of it taking on the ambience Saul had expressed a desire for.

Poised to make a good impression, Penny had the steak prepared to slide under the grill the moment she heard Saul's car enter the driveway.

'That smells good!'

It was a customary husbandly greeting, but not acompanied by the usual husbandly kiss as he walked past her into the dining-room.

'I hope it's tender.' Penny looked down at her offering anxiously, placing it before Saul as he sat down at the table, conscious of the fact that both of them seemed to be acting stereotype roles. At least, she consoled herself, it was more than she had hoped for after the cruel way he'd left her earlier that morning.

'Is anything wrong?' she ventured diffidently as he made no move to lift his knife and fork. Dear heaven, had she made some dreadful mistake? Perhaps he didn't like onions! She had married him after such a brief acquaintanceship she knew next to nothing of his tastes. Ironically, she would have been better placed to please him if he had employed her as a housekeeper. Then, presumably, he would have supplied her with a list of his likes and dislikes!

'No.' The curt reply was only partly reassuring as he surveyed her with restrained hostility. 'I'm merely waiting for you to join me at the table.'

'Oh!' Penny stared at him, totally at a loss. 'I'm not going to. I mean . . .' She stopped in mid-sentence. What she had meant was that she was still too confused and disturbed by what she had read in Tuppy's diary to have any appetite. Only she couldn't explain her lack of hunger in those precise words. Instead she substituted with a half-truth. 'Actually I ate out.'

'Did you?' The reply was uncompromisingly short. 'Tell me, Penny, does your idea of enjoying a platonic relationship with me embrace the thought that you shouldn't share the same table?'

'Of course not!' She met his narrowed gaze with spontaneous defiance, incensed by his deliberate incitement. 'It just means I'm not used to eating a large meal in the evenings.'

'Really? Why, Penny, were you too busy working—or enjoying yourself—to feed the inner woman?'

Saul didn't wait for an answer, which was just as well, Penny fumed in silent frustration at this patent attempt to ruffle her. It was as if he was being driven by some inner turmoil to rile her. Probably, she conceded with bitter acceptance, because she wasn't the woman he so desperately wanted her to be . . . only a poor facsimile of her beautiful sibling.

'Personally, I find little pleasure in solitary eating—so you can leave whatever you were about to do and join me.' He indicated the chair opposite him. 'Since we're engaged in a game of Happy Families let's play it according to the rules, shall we?'

There was no humour in the smile he bestowed on her, and only an aching emptiness in the light grey eyes that demanded her compliance.

'Tell me about your day, Penny.'

Obediently she pulled out a chair, sitting down and waiting until Saul lifted his knife and fork before speaking in her well modulated voice.

'The studio is beautiful, Saul,' she told him quietly. 'I never dreamed of having somewhere so ideal to work.

I'm very grateful . . .' She paused, inviting his comment, but when none was forthcoming she continued doggedly, 'I've sorted out all my tools and equipment. During the next few days I thought I'd get down to writing to my established customers and telling them my new address.'

'Good idea,' he returned equably, nodding his approval. 'This steak is excellent.' He paused. 'Have you spoken to Margaret today?'

'Just a quick phone call,' she confirmed. 'After I got back from the shops and started to cook your dinner. It's going to take me longer to get over to see Lucy from here . . .' She couldn't conceal the disappointment that coloured her voice. Her daily visits to see Lucy had sustained her for so long—and now, owing to the increased distance and the myriad household duties she had accepted, even *they* were going to have to be curtailed.

Saul lifted a casual shoulder. 'I can always run you over in the evening—if, of course, it's convenient for Margaret.'

'That's very good of you, Saul . . .' Penny bit her lip angrily, truncating her sentence in midstream. For that one moment she had forgotten how committed Saul himself was to the child. She swallowed her chagrin, annoyed at her own tactlessness. 'But she'd be asleep and I—we'd only disturb her.'

'Well, it won't be for long anyway. I spoke to my solicitor today. He wants to see you tomorrow to enable him to go ahead with your application.'

'Saul!' His name exploded from her lips. He had thrown the information at her so nonchalantly that if she hadn't known better she would have thought he didn't care one way or the other. 'Does he have any idea how long it will take?'

'No.' Saul shook his dark head. 'He warned me that the courts are heavily booked, but suggested that as your application will probably be heard privately in chambers he might be able to grab a cancellation if one comes up.' This time his smile was warm and generous as his sensuous mouth relaxed at her obvious excitement. 'He's a good man, Penny. He'll do his best for us, especially as I told him we've only recently been married and we want custody of Lucy as a special kind of Christmas gift—a kind of divine blessing on our union.'

There was so much pain and pride in his half-mocking avowal that Penny couldn't stop herself. Pushing her chair back, she darted round the table and flung her arms round his shoulders, pressing her warm cheek to his face, offering from the depths of her lonely heart the approval he was so desperately seeking, uncaring that she wasn't the source he sought.

'That's marvellous! Oh, I'm so happy!'

'Then I am too.' Slowly Saul rose to his feet, reaching out to hold her as she would have moved away. His firm hands gripped her shoulders as he gazed down at her glowing face. 'Don't pin all your hopes on being successful, pretty Penny. My solicitor feels our chances are excellent—but nothing in this life is guaranteed.'

Penny sighed softly. She didn't need reminding about life's vicissitudes. She had suffered too often and too deeply at their whims to be ignorant of their existence.

Returning Saul's steady appraisal, she saw that his warning had been meant kindly, perhaps as much a reminder to himself as her?

She rested her head against his shoulder, surprised yet

pleased to feel his arms slide round her body to embrace her.

'Being awarded guardianship would be the most wonderful Christmas of my life,' she whispered ecstatically. 'Or rather . . .' she dared to put a toe in the lake of his deceit, '*our* lives, Saul. Perhaps—perhaps if I'm given guardianship, in time we'll be able to adopt her—change her name officially to yours . . . that is, ours.' Her heart was beating nineteen to the dozen as she begged him silently to confide in her. 'That way we'd both have equal jurisdiction over her. She'd be recognised as ours, Saul . . . not just mine.'

She felt his body grow rigid, knew she had made a mistake even before the harshness of his reply confirmed her forebodings.

'Lucy has a name already—Michael's name!' Penny raised her head, stunned by his vehemence. 'Michael was illegitimate, abandoned by his mother as a baby and raised in a children's home. He had so little, I don't think we should erase his name from the records of life so totally.' There was a dark, forbidding anger in Saul's mesmerising eyes that made her cringe as he reinforced his avowal. 'It's not important to me what Lucy's surname is. Leave her the identity she was born with, Penny. It's what Tuppy would have wanted, I'm sure.'

He released his hold on her abruptly, walking away from the table to stand staring out over the garden, barely visible in the darkness of the autumn evening.

Penny felt as if she'd been slapped. All she had wanted to do was to make him see she was willing to share his daughter fully with him, and he had rebuffed her in the most hurtful way.

Obviously he was furious because she had dared

suggest they undo what had been Tuppy's decision. How deeply he must still care for her sister! Every word he spoke stirred up the latent jealousy that corroded her soul, forcing her to acknowledge what she much preferrred to relegate to the back of her mind.

In this instance the odds were that Saul was right—and the knowledge mortified her. Who was she to alter the choice Tuppy had made so painfully all those months ago?

Despite the central heating the room must have been cold, because Penny shivered. On the threshold of success, the last thing she wanted was to alienate Saul. She took a deep breath and forced herself to speak without rancour, changing the subject to divert his antagonism.

'I bought a Pavlova for dessert.'

The inconsequential statement dropped into the stretching silence.

'What?' Deep in this own thoughts, it seemed Saul hadn't even heard her, then he pushed a hand roughly through his hair as he turned to face her. 'Oh—I see. No, not for me, thanks. I prefer something more savoury. Cheese and biscuits, perhaps?'

'Of course,' she nodded. Walking with a careful dignity, she collected Saul's empty dessert plate and walked from the room.

In the kitchen the Pavlova sat on its plate—a mouthwatering concoction of cream, fruit and meringue, mocking her with its perfection.

Frustration and misery welled up inside her. Like Tantalus, the things she desired were so close to her—and like him, it seemed, she was about to find them always just out of reach.

Wasn't there any way at all she could reach through to Saul? If it was expecting too much for him to love her, couldn't she at least find the right things to do to make him like her?

Was she supposed to read something symbolical into his last assertion? she wondered irrationally. Yet another dig at her supposedly lurid past?

A deep sob burst from her throat as, in an untypical gesture of despair and exasperation, Penny smashed her fist down on the rejected dessert, promptly dissolving into tears as it disintegrated beneath her angry hand.

CHAPTER TWELVE

AT THE first sound of her alarm clock the following morning Penny leant across and switched it off. She had deliberately set it early so she could be out of the bathroom by the time Saul wanted to use it.

Masking a yawn with her hand, she forced herself to swing her legs out of bed, searching for her slippers with the toes of her bare feet. She had barely slept at all during the long doubt-filled night in which she had striven to find easy solutions to the problems lying ahead of her.

Still, she comforted herself, finding her pale blue satin mules and sliding her feet into them, Saul's ill-humour hadn't lasted too long. By the time she had cleared up the mess she had made in the kitchen and washed her hands and duly found a serving of cheese and biscuits he seemed to have regained his composure.

When she had finished clearing up after the meal she had joined him in the large sitting-room where they had spent the rest of the evening together in a companionable silence—Penny watching television while Saul buried himself in some technical magazines.

It had been eleven when, bored with the evening's programmes, Penny had announced her intention of going up to bed.

For one mad moment when Saul had yawned and answered laconically, 'Good idea, I think I'll join you,' she had imagined he was speaking literally, not metaphorically, and her heart leapt with a powerful surge of happiness, leaving her empty and disillusioned when he had walked past her room to his own, giving her a brief nod of his head and dismissing her presence with the trite exhortation that she should enjoy 'sweet dreams'.

From now on, she determined positively, wrapping her gown tightly round her, she was going to organise her life efficiently and independently of Saul as she had originally intended. And that, she told herself firmly, meant getting up early, providing a cooked breakfast for him and waving him goodbye at the door! Since she was to be only his housekeeper she would fulfil the role to the best of her ability!

The following days passed without incident. Not that there was much opportunity for confidences or altercations, Penny thought wryly. Saul left the house early each morning intent on solving the Middle East project he was working on with the minimum of delay, returning each evening to eat the carefully prepared meal she put before him with polite appreciation.

Afterwards they would sit in the same room reading or watching television until Penny, unable to bear Saul's emotional withdrawal, would quietly bid him goodnight and retire to her own lonely bed.

The interview with Saul's solicitor had gone off very well, and it was the prospect of the successful outcome of her application that kept Penny cheerful as she organised the housework so that she would leave herself ample time to pick up the threads of her business again.

Two weeks passed quickly as she steeled herself to accept things as they were, familiarising herself with the facilities of the nearby town and fitting in visits to Lucy whenever possible.

It was on one of her shopping expeditions that she had the idea of advertising her craft in a well-displayed shop window in the main street. When she had first launched out solo she had had some business cards printed giving her name and phone number. Altering the latter to her current number and displaying it prominently beneath her legitimate claim to be a member of the Guild of Glass Engravers, she returned home well pleased with herself.

She would show Saul she wasn't dependent on him for anything. Not money, not love . . . nothing!

A week later she was on the extension phone in the studio discussing a suitable engraving on a candlelamp with a new customer when she heard a car pull up outside, shortly followed by the sound of Saul's key in the lock.

Heavens! She'd been so engrossed in her work she hadn't realised how late it was. She hadn't even started on his dinner.

Awarding herself a black mark, Penny glanced down at her watch, startled to see she hadn't miscalculated. It seemed Saul had returned a lot earlier than usual.

'. . . For my wife . . .' the voice on the other end of the telephone was saying. 'It's our glass anniversary, so I want something romantic.'

Hearing Saul call out her name and then his footsteps mounting the stairs, Penny forced herself to pay attention to her caller.

'"Love is a growing or full constant light" is a popular quotation,' she told him, and heard his murmur of approval. 'If you'd like to see what it will look like, I have a sample lamp I can show you.' Her free hand reached out to a shelf to caress the delicate rim of fine English crystal.

Having already ascertained that her caller lived nearby she wasn't surprised to hear him accept her invitation eagerly. Her products weren't cheap and experience told her people liked to know in advance exactly what they were going to receive.

'Tomorrow at eleven a.m. then,' she agreed brightly. 'I'll be expecting you.'

She laid the phone back in its cradle and turned with a smile on her face to greet Saul, who had entered the room in time to catch the end of her conversation.

'Who was that?'

He made no move to approach her, standing motionless on the threshold, his light eyes brilliantly enquiring beneath level brows, taking in her appearance from the simple white sleeveless blouse she was wearing to the slim-cut aqua pants that fitted her slender hips and long legs as if they'd been custom tailored.

'A new client.' Penny saw the frown on his face deepen and added almost apologetically, 'I wasn't expecting you back so early, but it won't take me long to . . .'

'Obviously—or you wouldn't have been inviting your clients back to my house!'

Penny stared at him aghast. He had to be joking! But as electricity charged between them she knew with a bitter sense of helplessness that he wasn't. Anger overtook despair as she faced up to him.

'You're assuming, of course, that it was a man I was speaking to?'

'Wasn't it?' he fired back ruthlessly, daring her to lie.

Penny glared, knowing herself impotent against the impact of his belligerence. 'As a matter of fact it was,' she confirmed truculently. 'He saw my advertisement and wanted a surprise gift for his . . .'

'He saw your what!' There were granite chips in his clear eyes as Saul advanced into the room, catching hold of her wrist as she would have evaded him.

'My advertisement!' she flared back at him, refusing to be cowed by his unwarranted attitude. 'If you're supplying a service it has to be advertised. That's how businesses are built up!' She faced him defiantly, aware that he was burning with a slow anger, but totally unable to understand why. 'If you must know, I put a card in a shop window.'

'Dear God, Penny,' he breathed, his voice harshly censorious, 'what the hell do you think you're playing at?'

Furious tears stung her eyes. 'I'm playing at earning my own living—at not being a burden on you,' she flung back. 'You know as well as I that it was part of our agreement that I should continue with my engraving . . .' She made an angry gesture with her arm, encompassing the beautifully fitted out studio. 'Why else would you have provided me with all this?' Her voice shook as she met the hard implacability of his cold eyes. 'How I go about building up my business is nothing to do with you.'

'By marrying me you've made everything you do my concern,' Saul thrust back at her, releasing her wrist but remaining close to her, glowering down at her unrepentant face. 'Did it never occur to you that an advertisement in a shop window could attract all kinds of undesirables? What in damnation were you thinking about, Penny?' He uttered a deep sound of disgust in his throat. 'Inviting strangers to come and visit you when you were alone in the place!'

He might have a point there, Penny accorded silently, but no way was she kowtowing to the underlying aggression in his lecture and openly admitting it.

'I can look after myself,' she retorted with a show of bravado she was far from feeling. 'Besides, I'm very careful who I gave my address to. The man I was talking to was obviously genuine . . .'

'What a gift you must have—being able to divine virtue over a telephone wire!' His sarcastic retort denied her time to justify herself further. 'Even if you care so little for the preservation of your own skin, perhaps you ought to pause a while and consider Lucy's. She'll hardly be in a position to take care of herself if one of your callers should turn out to be less than genuine.'

'You make it sound as if I was offering a massage service instead of a perfectly legitimate product,' Penny mumbled unhappily, a feeling akin to panic making her wish there was more space between them as she was forced to yield to his logic. She had acted impulsively, spurred on by a deep need to prove she wasn't inadequate, and all she had accomplished was just the opposite as far as the dark-browed man she had married was concerned.

'That's another of your talents, is it?' Saul returned her mutinous scowl with a steady appraisal of his own. 'Then you'd most certainly be well advised not to make it generally known. If you need to keep your hand in, so to speak, you can always practise on me. God knows, I've had a frustrating enough day.'

He raised his hand to stroke the back of his neck, giving a rueful smile that drained away the coldness from his personable face.

'I'm sorry to disappoint you—I'm not qualified to help you.'

Penny swallowed back her sudden rush of sympathy, stilling the longing to hold out her arms to him, to cradle his dark head against her breasts. She might be no masseuse, but she had a woman's touch that would surely be able to ease the strain from Saul's face and comfort his strong body. She turned away from him. There was no future for either of them in letting him see the emotions that illuminated her face.

'No, of course not,' he agreed shortly. 'Put the suggestion down to wishful thinking on my part.' There was steel now in his clipped tones. 'I accept the need to market yourself, but I suggest you continue supplying your regular customers only for the time being. Once Lucy is here and you've established a routine for her, you can think again about building up your work level. If you still want to, I won't stand in your way but I will insist that any caller comes here by appointment in the evening when I'm in the house as well. Is that clear?'

'As crystal!' Resenting his tone, Penny seized the sample candlelamp from its shelf, holding it aloft between them, facetiously illustrating her reply, her blue eyes glinting with barely held fury.

'Excellent,' purred Saul, ignoring her bellicose stance. 'And you can make a start by phoning your recent caller and postponing his visit to the weekend.' He made a move as if to take the brandished lamp from her grasp. Obstinately Penny refused to relinquish it.

'No, I won't do that, Saul,' she told him coldly, determined not to let him wield total authority over her. 'I'm quite satisfied he's a genuine customer. There's no reason why I should put him off.'

'No?' Dark brows raised with mocking amusement. 'Not even if the guardianship hearing has been brought forward to tomorrow morning?'

'Oh!' She'd waited for so long for this day, but the cool

announcement flummoxed her. So this was the reason for Saul's early arrival. Rather than phone her he had preferred to tell her personally ... and then they'd become involved in an absurd argument ... 'But I'm not prepared ... I haven't thought out what to say or wear ... where do I have to go ... Oh dear, what time is it to be ...'

'Hey, hold on! There's no need for panic.' Saul's deep voice was warm and comforting. 'After all, this is what you've been waiting for all this time, and it's not as if you'll be facing it alone.'

'You're coming with me?' she asked tentatively. Somehow she had thought his work would be more important. Something he had said to her in passing the previous evening sprang to mind. 'But you've got an important appointment tomorrow,' she demurred.

'Don't be absurd, Penny!' Irritation spiced his reply. 'What's more important than settling Lucy's future?'

'Yes, of course.' She hung her head. Stupid, stupid Penny, she scolded herself silently. For a moment in her excitement she had forgotten how vested his own interest was.

If there was any real justice it would be Saul himself who was making the claim.

'Oh, Saul, I'm so afraid!' Suddenly she was unable to hide her anguish. 'Suppose I fail?'

'We can't ... we won't.' He was grimly optimistic as he reached forward to hold her upper arms, drawing her so close she could feel the heavy hammer of his heart against her own. 'Otherwise our whole marriage will be a mockery, won't it?'

His eyes laughed darkly into hers and in that instant Penny knew what he was going to do. Saw it in their glittering depths and in the open-lipped smile he gave her. She couldn't have stopped him even if she'd wanted to. As his mouth came down to possess her own expectant lips she tried desperately to replace the candlelamp on her work bench, thought she'd found the edge and, pushing it forward before releasing it, heard the glass shatter on the floor at her feet.

It didn't matter. Nothing mattered except the pressure of Saul's mouth on her own, the tender eagerness of his sweet tongue, the warm caressing movements of his sensitive hands as they travelled a path of fire down her back.

She could feel the heat of his aroused body glowing through his fine shirt as her hands crept beneath his jacket to capture his flesh and to adore it with her own soft fingers. The tide of longing he had conjured up that night of her surrender was rising again, flowing to full spate.

What did it matter if he didn't love her, that his arousal was more from anger at her thoughtless behaviour than desire? Anger was a powerful aphrodisiac, she'd been taught—he was her husband and she had enough love for both of them!

If Saul lifted her up into his arms and carried her triumphantly to his bedroom as he had that night in Paris, she would go willingly and stay as long as his need for her endured!

He didn't. He kissed her until she rested in his arms dazed and drained, then very gently he released her.

'Penny . . .' There was a dreadful hoarseness as he uttered her name. 'God forgive me, I didn't mean that to happen.'

Trying to assimilate the pain of his apology, deeply

hurt by his contrition, she watched with empty eyes as he swallowed deeply.

'I'll see you downstairs when you're ready. Don't forget to make that phone call, will you?'

With empty eyes, Penny watched him leave the room before kneeling down to gather the shards of glass at her feet. 'Love is a growing or full constant light' indeed—huh! With careful fingers she lifted the ruined shell and placed it in the waste bin. Seemingly her love for Saul was destined to be kept battened down in the darkness of her own heart until it withered away from lack of nourishment.

Slowly, she regained her feet and went to the phone.

The following day dawned cool and crisp.

Penny chose to wear the jade suit from her trousseau, hoping its obvious quality would give her the confidence she so badly needed. Little matter that Saul had explained it would be an informal hearing held in chambers; when the time came to go before the judge she was petrified.

As she sat in a daze, hardly taking in what was being said to her, only the most pertinent points seared their way into her consciousness. The favourable reports from the social services and the health visitor, the testimony from Lucy's foster-mother to her aunt's devotion and love, the judge's own certainty that by leaving Lucy in her care both the child's parents had intimated their love and trust.

Then he was looking up from his papers to smile at her. 'I'm perfectly satisfied that both you and your husband are willing and capable of giving this tragically orphaned little girl all the love and attention she has been so cruelly deprived of.' Wordlessly Penny's hand sought Saul's, feeling his fingers tighten round hers. 'Consequently I'm rescinding the "voluntary" care order placed on this child and granting the application of Mrs Saul van Diemen to assume guardianship over her.'

Outside chambers Penny could contain her joy no longer. Flinging her arms round Saul, she hugged him, experiencing a warm surge of pleasure at his instant response, the warmth of his arms locking against her, the solid bulk of his body giving her the physical support she needed as her knees buckled from sheer reaction.

Tears of happiness trailed a silver path down her cheeks as she raised her face, radiant with an inner joy, to meet the quiet asessment Saul bestowed on her.

'Oh, Saul . . .' she whispered. 'She's ours, really ours. Thank you for making it possible.'

There was a terrible irony in her gratitude. Saul had made it possible in more ways than one. A fierce stab of pain lanced through Penny's heart as she tried without success to read his feelings behind the cool withdrawn expression that held his features in perfect control.

If only she dared tell him what she had found out, invite his confidence and assure him of her loving support and compassion. The happiness died from her eager face. Saul had no use for her love—the disastrous aftermath of their one traumatic union had proved that beyond doubt, she reminded herself sadly.

Neither was it the time or place to incite a confrontation. So when he gently disengaged her from his embrace and took her arm to lead her out into the cool dampness of the London street, she followed him silently.

'I planned on a celebration being in order, so I've reserved a table for lunch,' he told her pleasantly, guiding her across the busy street.

'Lovely!' Penny smiled her pleasure. 'I'd like to tell Margaret the result, if you don't mind. She asked me to phone her when I went there yesterday afternoon.'

'I thought of that too.' Saul slanted her an understanding smile. 'There's a phone in the restaurant you can use.'

Minutes later she was dialling Margaret's number.

'We won!' she announced as soon as the receiver was lifted.

'I always knew it!' Margaret Stanley sounded as delighted as Penny felt. 'They made a big mistake taking her away from you in the first place. Even if you and Saul hadn't got married when you did I'm sure she'd have been returned to you.'

'Well, being Mrs Saul van Diemen clinched it, I think.' Give the handsome devil she'd married his due, she thought with a painful affection. God knew how she would have fared without his supportive presence. 'I'm sorry?' She was suddenly aware that Margaret had asked her a question while she'd been occupied with her thoughts of Saul.

'Gordon and I want you both to come over and see us tonight. You can tell Lucy the good news yourself— although she won't understand a word of it, of course— and then we'll have a little drink to celebrate and you can tell me all about Paris.'

'That's very sweet of you, Margaret.' Penny hesitated. 'I'll have to ask Saul. He may be going back to the office and working late.'

'Nonsense!' Margaret's reply was brisk. 'The man's head over heels in love with you, my dear. He won't leave your side in your moment of triumph, take my word for it! Besides, there'll be some paperwork necessary before you can take Lucy back with you—and you haven't been to see her today, have you?'

Head over heels indeed! Penny sighed as she replaced the receiver. For a perceptive woman Margaret Stanley was peculiarly blind where Saul was concerned, but then she wouldn't be the first woman to read what she wanted into those classically moulded features, or the last woman to be deceived by her own hopes.

Slowly Penny made her way back to the restaurant her heart plummeting with a surge of love for the taciturn man who sat so composedly studying the menu awaiting her return.

It was late when they arrived back home.

'I'm sorry, Saul,' Penny apologised with an uncertain smile. 'I'm afraid I let my tongue run away with me.' She thought guiltily of the way she had enthused over Paris to the Stanleys. Whether it was excitement, relief or the two glasses of Scotch Margaret had insisted on her drinking to salute her new status, she couldn't say, but it seemed she just hadn't been able to stop talking.

'It was a pleasant evening.' He shrugged away her apology, but she could see from the strained lines of his face that he was tired. 'And very gratifying to learn that you took so much pleasure from our honeymoon.'

Penny looked away, unable to meet his gaze, hating his dry irony as much as her own feelings of despair. How much longer could she go on with this tissue of deceit lying between them?

'I don't think I'll ever forget it,' she told him tersely. Let him make what he would of that! 'And now, if you've no objections, I'd like to get some sleep.'

She walked away from him, wishing he would stop her

and knowing he wouldn't. Upstairs she went through the ritual of preparing for bed, her heart heavy.

Saul and she were no more than polite strangers now, a deep void of secrecy and non-communication dividing them. What kind of home would she be bringing Lucy back to? she wondered dully. Despite its beauty and actual warmth, the elegant and comfortable furnishings that reflected Saul's taste and ability to purchase the best, it would be a sterile place to bring up a child without the existence of emotional warmth between the two adults who both cared for her.

Penny shivered as she climbed beneath the duvet. For so long she had put all her energies into the goal of winning Lucy. Now she had attained it she was having doubts.

As Lucy grew up in their care, wouldn't she sense the friction between herself, Penny, and Saul and be disturbed by it?

Restlessly she turned over on to her other side. She could only pray that her own love for both of them would be enough to maintain an ambience of harmony.

CHAPTER THIRTEEN

THREE HOURS later sleep had still not come to Penny. Lying awake listening to the small noises of the night, she had heard Saul enter the room next to her an hour or so previously. Now the ticking of her clock was a monstrous sound in the stillness of the night.

Inevitably she remembered the last time she had been intimidated by its monotonous rhythm—and what had happened when she had left the room to escape it. If only she could go to Saul now, hold him, comfort him, bring his strong male body to fulfilment as she had done then! Horrified at how her wanton thoughts had affected her body, she felt her breasts tightening and experienced again the warm tantalising thrill that made her want to savour his nearness.

Painfully she recalled Saul's contemptuous words 'when you wake up in the morning it's to me you'll have to come'. Never, she thought violently, because it wasn't just his body she ached to possess but his heart and his soul. She longed to fill the gaps in his life so cruelly created by other people's actions, to give as much as to take.

She needed to break through the barriers Saul had erected. Only once or twice had she glimpsed the compassion and sensitivity which lurked behind the cool façade he presented to the world, and if she hadn't wanted him to trust her with his innermost secrets she wouldn't have loved him as much as she did.

Oh, this was useless! She hadn't wanted to have recourse to sleeping tablets, but twice in several weeks would hardly make a junkie of her. Swinging her legs out of bed, she located her handbag with the panacea she sought. Quietly opening the door on to the darkened hallway on her way to the bathroom for water, she saw the light seeping from beneath Saul's door.

Her heart seemed to miss a beat. If Saul was still awake, tortured by his own memories, this could be the opportunity she needed to persuade him to confide in her so she could assure him that although guardianship had been vested in her she would never deny him a real interest in his daughter's future.

Without giving herself a chance to think again she tapped lightly on the door.

'Come in, Penny—what's wrong? Don't you feel well?'

Saul was sitting up in bed with a book still in his hand, his gaze, as he turned towards the doorway which framed her, concerned.

'I'm all right.' Nervously Penny moistened her dry lips. She could feel his eyes boring into her as she stared back at him, his upper body tanned and muscular against the whiteness of the base sheet.

Was it really such a short time since she had first seen him stripped to the waist in this very room? Beneath his piercing appraisal she shivered, wishing she had thought to put on a wrap over her flimsy nightdress and hoping against hope that her courage wouldn't fail her at this crucial moment.

'I saw your light on,' she faltered. 'And I thought perhaps there were things we should discuss before Lucy arrives.'

'Confession time?' Saul's mouth tightened in a face

that had suddenly grown hard.

Penny's fingers curled apprehensively into her palms. At least he hadn't pretended she wanted to talk about feeding routines!

'Sit down, Penny.' He indicated the bed as he placed the now closed book on the table beside it. 'If we're to have a heart-to-heart talk at least let's be on the same level.'

Silently she obeyed him, her heart hammering a wild tattoo. The expression on his face wasn't easily definable, yet it brought a curious feeling of helplessness to plague her.

'As a matter of fact I couldn't sleep either—and no doubt for the same reason ... wondering how we can hope to be a complete family, let alone a happy one, with so much unacknowledged anguish still an insurmountable barrier between us.'

This was it, then—the confession she had both longed for and dreaded. Penny's hands gripped each other so fiercely she felt her nails pierce the soft palms.

'Go on,' she whispered huskily, her heart continuing to thunder its fast disturbing rhythm as she braced herself to hear and accept the truth.

Saul shook his dark head wearily. 'Oh, Penny, don't look at me like that, I'm not going to hurt you ... You see, I've known for a long time it was Michael you were waiting for here on my bed that afternoon.'

'What!' Penny fought blind panic to keep her self-control as pale colour began to creep up beneath the alabaster whiteness of her cheeks and her blue eyes widened in horrified astonishment.

There was no anger in Saul's deep voice, just a deep resignation. 'You don't have to deny it, Penny. After I left you I passed him on the stairs . . .'

'No!' Furiously she tried to gain her feet, only to be forcibly restrained as Saul's hand whipped out to grip her shoulders with powerful fingers.

'For God's sake, Penny, you don't have to lie to me! If we're to have any useful future together we have to make a new start—be totally honest with each other!'

She shook her head in bewilderment, her throat too choked with emotion to interrupt as he continued gently,

'Oh, at first I thought you'd made some rendezvous with one of the guests for fun.' His mouth twisted wryly at her shocked intake of air. 'It was just the sort of game Samantha loved playing—slipping away at a party, stripping off, lying naked between the sheets of her host's bed, waiting for him . . . But I was the host that day, and you certainly hadn't made any arrangements with me! The more I thought about it the more I realised it must have been Michael you were waiting for. He was always talking about you, praising your work, telling me how lovely you were, and I knew you'd stepped into Tuppy's shoes when she'd had to go back to hospital that time.'

Doggedly ignoring her obvious agitation, he continued brutally, 'Michael knew my house—knew the layout. He would have known where my bedroom was and the unlikelihood of being disturbed there.' To Penny's agonised gaze his breathing became laboured, hinting at a distress already beginning to show on the lean lines of his face. 'He was about to leave England for three weeks . . . three weeks without the sight and sound of you. I imagine he must have been just desperate enough to want to spend his last moments in England with you . . . to love you . . .'

'Stop it!' Penny's anguish was reflected in her face as

at last she found the power of speech as Saul's voice broke and faltered. 'Michael was my brother-in-law and nothing else . . . ever!'

This time she *had* to explain her seemingly bizarre behaviour and pray Saul would believe her! She was shaking with tension as fury sharpened her voice.

'I told you the dress I was wearing was a gift. So it was—a gift from Tuppy. She thought I was plain and drab and she wanted me to be glamorous when she introduced me to the fabulous Saul van Diemen . . .' Her tone sawed with raw emotion. 'She bought a basque for me to wear underneath it . . . I guess she thought it would make me feel feminine and desirable . . . but I wasn't used to squeezing myself into such a constricting garment. I wanted to please her, but after a while I couldn't even breathe properly . . .'

Penny gulped to stop the angry tears that threatened her from falling. 'All I wanted to do was get the wretched thing off and take out the rigid stays so I could go down and enjoy the party . . .'

She stopped speaking as heavy sobs prevented further words. Saul had thought *that* of her! Not only had he seen her as amoral but as a husband-stealer too—and even worse—the thief of her own sister's husband! No wonder he had treated her with such cruel disdain. A flush of shame stained her cheeks as she condemned herself for not telling him the truth earlier . . . but then she had never suspected the depths to which he had believed she had sunk.

It was like receiving a knock-out blow, but it was nothing compared to the effect on Saul of her denial, she realised as she gazed bitterly at his stunned face.

'You're telling me you and Michael weren't even in

love? That my accidental arrival in the room didn't spoil your final goodbye?'

'Yes!' she blazed up at him fiercely. 'How dare you accuse me of such a dreadful thing . . .'

'Listen to me, Penny!' There was a tense excitement thickening his speech as his fingers dug deeply into her soft flesh. 'I've believed all these weeks that one of your reasons—perhaps the strongest—for wanting Lucy so much was because she's Michael's daughter, and you wanted something to remember him by . . . something live and beautiful . . .'

'No.' Penny spoke flatly, awed by the pain and passion that lay behind his wild surmise. Too moved by his obvious suffering she felt her anger wilting. 'No,' she repeated softly. 'I wanted Lucy for herself because I love her.' And then, as an odd light seemed to illuminate the steady grey eyes that surveyed her unblinkingly, she knew that because she loved him, she had to make it easy for him.

She reached out one of her hands and touched his cheek. 'Oh, Saul . . . I know you and Tuppy had an affair when she was already with Michael, and that when she became pregnant you asked her to marry you, but she refused . . .' The stillness of his carven face wasn't encouraging, but she knew Saul was right. It was imperative that the truth was finally brought out into the light.

She took a deep breath to steady her ragged nerves. 'I know Lucy isn't Michael's child . . . that she's *your* daughter, Saul.'

'Penny . . .' His voice choked on her name. Impulsively she rushed to reassure him.

'I promise I'll never take her away from you. I know

how much you must have loved Tuppy, that I can never replace her in your heart or your life . . . but I loved her too . . .' Tears started to spill down her anxious face. 'Oh, Saul, I understand how you must feel . . .'

'Do you?' Saul's hands hurt her shoulders as with a sudden passion he jerked her to him. The eyes that bored into her own were grim and foreboding as her senses leapt and her heart began to race anew. 'Then this won't come as a surprise to you, my crazy, muddle-headed wife!'

As one arm encircled her body like a steel band, Saul flung the duvet off the bed, moving to trap her body beneath him with hard-muscled legs while his mouth sought and devoured hers with a savage passion.

Lying beneath him, powerless to move, terrifyingly aware of the potency that surged through his naked body, Penny felt one hand seek and grasp her breast, feeling its way through the transparent covering to caress its aching pinnacle with surprising tenderness.

Instinctively her lips parted as her senses reacted to Saul's heady nearness. It had been so long without him she had no thought but to submit to his demanding strength.

For breathless minutes he drained her desire, exciting her breasts, taunting the heart of her passion with the force of his own arousal as her body arched to meet him.

Then suddenly, devastatingly, he was rolling away from her and she was left gasping and unsatisfied, her hair wild, her eyes semi-focused, her mouth throbbing.

'Now,' he said harshly, grey eyes glittering with a febrile threat as she strove to regain composure, 'tell me what the hell you're talking about—and fast! Because I can assure you I was never in love with your sister and I most certainly didn't seduce her!'

Oh, if only she could believe that! Instinctively Penny cowered away from Saul's patent anger, but she had gone too far to retract now.

'I have proof.' Her reply was low, pain-racked, as she called his bluff. 'It was all written down in her diary: how she went to bed with you and afterwards when you found out she was pregnant you begged her to be your wife.' With agonised eyes she met his glowering appraisal. Surely he had too much honour than to label her dead sister a liar?

The sigh of exasperation he breathed racked his strong body. 'Listen to me, Penny.' He was so intense, his face so white and drawn, for a moment she thought he was going to strike her, but when his hand flashed out it was only to hold her chin to turn her face towards his. 'The only person I begged your sister to marry was Michael.' Saul stared down at her pale face, his eyes darkened by a powerful emotion. 'And the only time Tuppy was ever in my bed was when I took her out to dinner shortly after Michael told me he meant to marry her. She passed out in the restaurant of the hotel where I was staying. It seemed the simplest thing to do to take her to my room and summon the hotel doctor.' He made an impatient gesture with his free hand. 'Only after a very short while she was totally recovered, so instead I sent her home in a taxi and told her to see her own doctor.'

'The only time Tuppy ever fainted was in the early days of her pregnancy ...' Wide-eyed, her breath catching in her throat, Penny met the eyes that begged her trust, the words no more than a whisper as the ambiguous phrases Tuppy had written formed another pattern ...

'Yes.' There was a dark anguish now in the tortured male face so close to her own. 'Your sister was already carrying Lucy when I met her by chance and on an impulse took her out to dinner to warn her against marrying a man who was still on the beginning of the road to success and who would be unable to devote every minute of his time to her . . . only neither of us knew her condition then.'

'You—you warned her off Michael?' Bewildered and uncomprehending, Penny stared back at his troubled eyes.

'Yes.' Saul voiced the bleak affirmative with obvious effort. 'Dear God, Penny . . . I have no excuses. She was pretty, volatile, full of high spirits. She reminded me of Samantha.' He swallowed with difficulty. 'I thought she was a good-time girl, and I didn't want Michael to make the same mistake I had. But I was wrong . . . horribly wrong. I didn't have to be with her for long before I realised what a dreadful mistake I'd made. But it was too late. By then she truly believed she would be a burden on Michael's future career prospects. Although I hadn't realised then how deeply my comments had penetrated.'

Poor Tuppy! Of course she would never have shown the depth of her reactions to a comparative stranger. Few people ever guessed how tender her heart was beneath her bright, extrovert exterior. And poor Saul . . . His good intentions another paving stone on the road to his own private hell . . .

His steady voice penetrated Penny's musings. 'When I realised I was responsible for Tuppy's continual refusal to marry Michael and saw how it was tearing him apart, I went to her and begged her to reconsider her decision.' He paused as a wild, surging joy began to feed its way through Penny's whole being. 'I managed to persuade her that she and the baby were everything Michael wanted . . . and needed . . . and she agreed on condition that I'd be the child's godfather to prove my sincerity.'

Blindly Penny blinked away her tears, momentarily bereft of words.

'And that, my pretty Penny, was the beginning of all my own troubles!' Saul gathered her unresisting body into his arms, holding her to him so that she could feel the steady thud of his heart against her own. Gentle caressing hands smoothed her back as his voice thickened. 'Because *you* burst into my life—the lovely, shy, talented sister I'd heard so much about that I was already half in love with her before I set eyes on her! I wasn't prepared for the heady vision you made in your figure-hugging dress—a potent temptation for any red-blooded man.' A slight smile turned the corners of his mouth. 'But this time I wasn't going to make the judgements of a man who was used to assessing all women on the precedent of an amoral cheating wife whose pleasures lay in the wilder perversions of so-called love!'

'I'm not like that . . . oh, Saul!' It was a broken cry from her heart as Penny felt the tremor that shook Saul's body. 'I'm not like that . . . I never was . . .'

'Do you think I don't know that now?' The harshness of his reply was punishing in its rasping power. 'But *then*, dear lord, I went into my bedroom and there you were, revealed in all your breathtaking loveliness . . . and I was shattered! Torn between anger because after all you *were* another Samantha and jealousy because it wasn't me you were waiting for . . . and I wished like hell it had been!'

Penny buried her auburn head against his naked

shoulder, inhaling the sweet scent of his skin. How cruel the humiliations Samantha must have forced on him to bring about such a wild surmise, such tortuous logic. Loving him as she did, Penny could almost understand . . . certainly forgive.

'Believing what you did, why on earth did you decide to marry me?' Puzzled blue eyes pleaded for an explanation.

'So many reasons . . .' Saul gave a brief derisive bark of laughter. 'Because you were right—I did have a responsibility towards Lucy and your suggestion was the only way I could discharge it . . . because after ignoring all my attempts to help you, you sat there looking so frail and drawn, and I wanted to slap you for being so foolishly headstrong, but more than that, I wanted to take you in my arms and comfort you—but mostly because I desired you with every fibre of my body that made me a man!'

Penny shivered uncontrollably at the vehemence of his tone and felt his arm tighten round her.

'Oh, I was angry with you . . . sitting there offering me a cold-blooded arrangement when my blood was on fire for you . . . giving me no credit for having feelings of my own. Michael had been my friend as well as my colleague! Do you think I hadn't had my own fair share of sleepless nights?'

Shifting miserably against Saul's warm body, Penny was engulfed by guilt at the note of hurt in his deep voice. How could she have been so immersed in her own agony as not to have realised how Saul was suffering behind his patina of composure? She hadn't been the only one to be blind.

'Don't you see, Penny, I was caught in a trap of my

own making. I wanted to make you confess your love for Michael, and yet I didn't want to hear you say it. I wanted to give Lucy a permanent home, yet I was tortured by my beliefs that you'd loved Michael and she would always be a constant reminder of that love. But uppermost in my mind was the fact that I wanted you and the realisation that I had to act fast before you offered yourself to some other man to get the security you needed.'

Unhappily Penny choked on her chagrin. Saul *had* wanted her—but having taken her, possessed her body with a fierce driving need, somehow he had found her wanting. Somehow she had failed him——

'I should have told you right from the start why I was half naked in your bedroom . . .' Her voice trembled with despair.

Saul didn't deny it, as he moved his hand to touch the russet silk of her hair. 'Even when I discovered for myself that you'd never known any man, I still believed it was Michael you cared for and that it was my untimely interruption that had kept you apart. How can I ever expect you to forgive me?'

A second rush of tears scalded Penny's face. Saul was baring his innermost soul to her, inviting her scorn, laying himself open to her bitter condemnation . . . and she was finding his suffering unbearable.

'I can forgive you anything, Saul,' she assured him. 'You see . . .' She was about to tell him she loved him, but he broke into her words, his tone heavy with a puissant self-disgust.

'Even rape?' Then as her mouth opened in horrified but silent protest, he went on doggedly, 'Do you think I can ever forgive myself for forcing myself on you,

knowing you'd only come to me because you thought I'd
go back on my word? All I could think of that night was
holding you, taking you, hearing you say my name with
desire and need as I held you beneath me and discovered
your inner warmth as I'd already discovered the outer
warmth. My God!' His voice shook with raw pain. 'I've
been living with the guilt of my brutality like a millstone
round my neck. I love you, Penny . . . and I raped you.'

'No!' She was reaching out to him, flinging her arms
round him, drawing him to her. 'Oh, my darling, darling
love, it wasn't like that!'

Love? Saul had said he loved her? Not need or desire
this time . . . but love! Penny held her wild mounting joy
in check as for the first time she began to understand the
meaning of those silent withdrawn days after their wild
union. 'Oh, my sweet love,' she crooned, drawing the
dark head to her breast, stroking the thick dark hair as it
lay black as a raven's wing against her pale flesh. 'It was
never like that . . .'

'I hurt you badly, Penny.' He refused her exoneration,
but his lips moved momentarily against her skin,
savouring its sweet fragrance. 'The memory of your
tears, and your pain the next morning, will haunt me for
the rest of my life.'

A tremendous wave of exultation swept through her as
Penny moved her hands to caress the smooth skin of his
shoulders, feeling their tenseness beneath her palms.
When she spoke it was softly but with great determination, and total honesty.

'Your floor was a little uncomfortable . . . but *you*
Saul . . . *you* were magnificent.' She touched the midnight bristle of his jaw with soft fingers. 'Haven't you
ever heard of tears of joy?'

There was a poignant silence before Saul spoke, pain in every syllable. 'Don't give me your pity, Penny. I don't deserve it . . . and I don't think I can handle it.'

'Not pity, Saul . . . love.'

She had wanted to tell him for so long, and the words felt so marvellous she said them again softly and sweetly.

'I love you, Saul.' Sliding her hands round his heated flesh, feeling the fierce tremor that ran down his lean length, and knowing triumphantly that he could read the truth in her shining eyes. That at last he believed her.

'You're tired, my darling wife . . .' Saul pulled the neck of Penny's nightdress down past her shoulders to pay homage to the pale orbs of her full breasts, his thumbs moving with impossible delicacy as they aroused hot cords of fire which streamed through her, while a deep yawning ache swelled inside her.

'So are you, beloved husband . . .' Reading his diffidence for the concern on her behalf which it was, Penny reached her hands to his waist, moving them downwards, exhilarated by the power of his response to their trembling approach. 'But, like you . . . not *too* tired.'

Saul uttered a sound, half groan, half sob, as he accepted her invitation with restrained greed and exquisite tenderness.

All the anguish, the weeks of suffering had been worth this culmination of ecstasy, Penny thought later as, blissfully happy, she lay naked against Saul's powerful passionate body, heart to heart, skin to skin, knowing that at last she had convinced him utterly that he was both her servant and her master, her beloved conqueror whose strength and passion were too welcome invaders ever to cause her pain.

There remained one nagging worry to torment her as,

on the brink of sleep, she lifted her head slightly to gaze down into Saul's smooth relaxed face, with troubled eyes.

'Do you think Tuppy and Michael would ever forgive us if they knew what we'd been thinking about them?' she asked him anxiously.

'I'm sure they would.' The comforting answer came swiftly. 'Especially since it's clear now that they always intended you and me to meet and fall in love with each other. Of course,' he continued thoughtfully, 'I imagine they'd insist on a token of our good faith for the future—like our providing Lucy with a permanent playmate. What do you think, my love?'

'I think it's the least we could do for them.' Penny answered him seriously, smiling as she heard his soft purr of laughter, and he pulled her down so that her lips hovered above his own.

'For them—for Lucy——' he told her softly. 'But most of all—for us, my pretty Penny.

Then he reached for her mouth with his own and sealed their decision with a kiss.

Mills & Boon

YOU'RE INVITED TO ACCEPT **FOUR ROMANCES** AND A TOTE BAG **FREE!**

Acceptance card

| NO STAMP NEEDED | Post to: Reader Service, FREEPOST, P.O. Box 236, Croydon, Surrey. CR9 9EL |

Please note readers in Southern Africa write to:
Independant Book Services P.T.Y., Postbag X3010, Randburg 2125, S. Africa

YES! Please send me 4 free Mills & Boon Romances and my free tote bag – and reserve a Reader Service Subscription for me. If I decide to subscribe I shall receive 6 new Romances every month as soon as they come off the presses for £7.20 together with a FREE monthly newsletter including information on top authors and special offers, exclusively for Reader Service subscribers. There are no postage and packing charges, and I understand I may cancel or suspend my subscription at any time. If I decide not to subscribe I shall write to you within 10 days. Even if I decide not to subscribe the 4 free novels and the tote bag are mine to keep forever. I am over 18 years of age   EP20R

NAME _____

(CAPITALS PLEASE)

ADDRESS _____

_____

_____ POSTCODE _____

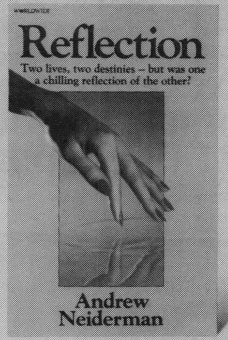